Inside the
Science Museum

Published 2001 by NMSI Trading Ltd,
Science Museum, Exhibition Road, London SW7 2DD.
All rights reserved

Compiled by Louise Wilson, from material supplied by curators and other staff of
the Science Museum.

Edited by Giskin Day.

Photographs courtesy of the Science & Society Picture Library, Science Museum,
Exhibition Road, London SW7 2DD.
Tel +44 (0)20 7942 4400; Fax +44 (0)20 7942 4401
E-mail piclib@nmsi.ac.uk; Website http://www.nmsi.ac.uk/piclib
Additional photography by David Exton, Claire Richardson and Andreas Schmit.
Cover photograph by Andreas Schmit.

Designed by DS Print and Redesign.

Printed in Belgium by Snoeck-Ducaju & Zoon.

© 2001 Board of Trustees of the Science Museum

ISBN 1 900747 19 7

Website: http://www.sciencemuseum.org.uk

Contents

Foreword

The Science Museum is a unique institution. Its vast collections are a record of an astonishing historical phenomenon – the emergence of the first industrial society.

The Museum has been adding to its collections for 150 years. Each generation of curators selects and acquires objects – inventions, images, contraptions, products, ephemera – the material signature of time. This cumulative legacy provides the physical sources from which to construct new histories, new stories and new meanings, as each generation seeks to make sense of its own world and tell the story of its time.

The collections contain some 6 million items: physical objects, photographs and archives. Among the 300,000 physical artefacts are more 'world firsts' than are held by any other science museum. The exhibition galleries, in which a small part of the collections is displayed and interpreted, occupy some seven acres of public display space (about 30,000 square metres) and cover major themes in science, technology and medicine. The galleries offer examples of how objects, through interpretation, can be used to provide an understanding of contemporary life.

The most recent addition to the Museum is the Wellcome Wing, which opened to the public in July 2000. This dramatically distinctive new space is devoted to contemporary science and technology. Displays are constantly renewed to reflect the changing frontiers of science, and to track the latest developments in laboratory research and industry. Interactive exhibits are used to engage visitors with issues and choices. Art installations stimulate reflection and challenge received perceptions.

Museums have many identities – cathedral, warehouse and fairground. There is reverence for learning, history, achievement and, perhaps, some humility at the incompleteness of our own understanding. A museum is a repository – a storehouse – of physical evidence. It is also a place of fun and enjoyment.

Those of us who have the privilege of caring for, building and interpreting the collections wish, wherever possible, to share with visitors the fascination, insights and enjoyment that come from daily contact with modern and historical artefacts of science and technology. This book is a tribute to invention and ingenuity. It is also a reflection of the rewarding relationship between people and things – a small celebration of the Science Museum for those who visit and may wish to take a little of their experience away with them.

Doron Swade
Assistant Director & Head of Collections

Industry and technology

The collections of the Science Museum chronicle the development of technology, science and industry. This section of the book features tools and machines that changed the manufacturing industry as well as engines that provided new means of power and transport. Some of the products and artwork inspired by the changes in the Industrial Revolution are also highlighted. We discuss a few of the inventions and discoveries that have formed Western lives, including innovations that led to changes in medicine and communication. Finally, more recent technological developments have been chosen to represent ongoing changes in transport, space technology and biotechnology.

Coalbrookdale by Night

The Severn Gorge in Shropshire was remarkable in the late eighteenth and early nineteenth century for the concentration of industry, mainly ironmaking, along three miles of the Severn valley between Coalbrookdale and Coalport. Coalbrookdale was an example of this new industry that was spreading through Britain. There were many new uses for iron, such as iron rails, the first iron bridge and the steam railway locomotive, so this area attracted engineers from Britain and abroad who visited and wrote accounts of what they saw. The Coalbrookdale experience was also recorded by many artists, who found the combination of the area's natural topography and the human influence of fire and smoke from the furnaces a fascinating spectacle. This painting, *Coalbrookdale by Night*, by Philippe Jacques de Loutherbourg in 1801, shows the buildings of an ironworks silhouetted against the fire from what is thought to be Bedlam furnaces.

Arkwright's spinning machine

Sir Richard Arkwright's spinning machine, and the factories built up to exploit it, suddenly changed the domestic tradition of spinning yarn at home. This model is thought to be a prototype from around 1769 as it corresponds closely to Arkwright's patent drawing from this time. In spinning, the fibres have to be 'drafted' (teased out) and then twisted together. In the machine, pairs of 'drafting rollers' do the work that was done by the spinner's fingers.

Many spinning machines were grouped together under one roof and were driven by a central power source, initially horse power. In 1771, a larger water-powered mill was built at Cromford in Derbyshire, and this design became known as a 'water frame'. Arkwright licensed the use of his invention in units of 1000 spindles, and many of the remains of early spinning mills in the north Midlands are thought to have been built to house water frames.

Nasmyth's steam hammer

James Nasmyth (1808–1890) was both an engineer and an artist. His 1871 painting of one of his steam hammers is a portrayal of industrial production on a grand scale. The people in this picture appear almost as slaves of the industrial machinery, feeding it with the raw products it requires (in this case a massive iron bar) to manufacture engine and machine parts. The steam hammer gave the smith the power to forge a larger mass of iron or steel, and to handle larger components than had previously been possible.

A Manufacturing Town

L S Lowry became famous for his depictions of northern textile towns, including his native Salford. This 1922 oil painting contains many elements characteristic of his later work: factory buildings, smoking chimneys and large numbers of people on the streets. Whereas Lowry's paintings have sometimes been criticised as reflecting his own reclusive nature, it was conventional in this period to focus on the negative impact of industrialisation and to locate the causes of contemporary problems in the past.

Davy's safety lamp

In the eighteenth century, miners worked by the light of naked flames, such as candles. As increased demands for coal during the Industrial Revolution meant that mines became deeper, a new danger manifested itself in the form of a gas, composed mainly of methane, called firedamp, found in the fissures of coal seams. Firedamp becomes explosive when exposed to air and can be ignited by a naked flame. Many miners were killed in pit explosions, including 92 men and boys at Felling Colliery in 1812. The outcry led to the establishment of the Sunderland Society for Preventing Accidents in Coal Mines. In 1815 the society approached Sir Humphry Davy for help. He carried out experiments on samples of firedamp and found that perforated metal or wire gauze will so cool a flame attempting to pass through it that ignition of flammable gases is prevented. Davy designed a lamp with its central flame surrounded by brass wire gauze, and this is one of his first two experimental lamps actually to be used in a coal mine. Most later safety lamps were based on its design.

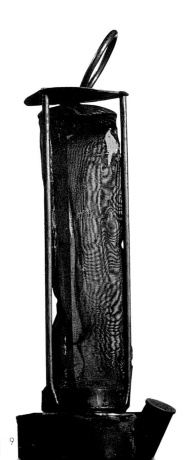

Troughton's dividing engine

In 1774, instrument maker Jesse Ramsden completed a successful 'circular dividing engine', a machine for setting out the graduations on the scales of instruments for measuring angles. Previously the scales of such instruments were graduated by hand, which was tedious work for skilled men and consequently expensive. Using the engine, scales could be drawn accurately and quickly. This development was very important, since instruments such as the sextant were in demand for the new methods of finding longitude at sea, which contributed greatly to the safety of shipping and to the success of voyages of discovery. In recognition of the national importance of his invention, Ramsden was rewarded by the government for making his invention public. John Troughton, an established competitor of Ramsden's, built this engine as a near copy. It seems that many instrument makers preferred to have their work graduated on this dividing engine rather than on Ramsden's, possibly because Troughton provided a quicker service.

Portsmouth block-making machinery

This machinery was invented by Marc Isambard Brunel and built by Henry Maudslay in 1803 for the British navy. It marked a new approach to manufacturing and the first coherent application of mass production. The navy required huge numbers of wooden pulley-blocks – there are nearly a thousand in the rigging of a ship such as HMS *Victory* – which were previously supplied by contractors who made them mainly by hand. The block-making machines each performed a single operation on a block, which was then passed to the next machine. All the processes, except the final light finishing and assembly, were mechanised. The quality of the blocks produced was more consistent: ten men working the machines had the same output as 110 skilled men working by hand. In the 'shaping engine' seen here, the outsides of ten block shells at a time were cut to shape. The shells were fixed into a cage, which was rotated by a steam engine. They were then trimmed by a cutter, which was moved by hand but guided mechanically by templates. The inset shows a completed pulley block made on this machinery.

Lathe by Maudslay

The Science Museum is proud to own a number of examples of the work of Henry Maudslay (1771–1831), who was one of the founders of modern machine-building. His improvements to the lathe, the basic machine tool, were revolutionary. This example (above) incorporates a slide rest, which Maudslay developed. By mechanically guiding the cutting tool, the slide rest enabled the turner to work with greater accuracy. Among other tools by Maudslay, who was a stickler for precision and a pioneer of all-metal machinery, are some developed for the important task of making accurate screws (left) – the foundation of accuracy in machine tools. Maudslay's workshop was the 'school' for many of the important British engineers of the nineteenth century.

Bessemer converter

In 1856, Henry Bessemer developed a converter to manufacture bulk steel, which is produced by reducing the quantity of carbon in cast iron. The converter worked by blowing air through molten iron, which oxidised the carbon out of the iron. Prior to Bessemer's invention, engineers used wrought iron, which was tough but expensive, or cast iron, which was hard but brittle. Steel was only available in small quantities of unreliable quality. Several ironmasters approached Bessemer for patent rights to his converter but, when they conducted their own experiments, they invariably failed. It was later discovered that only low-phosphorous iron ore could produce quality steel. Such low-phosphorous deposits could be found in the Lake District, England, where the Barrow Haematite Ironworks began experiments in 1864 using this small converter. The first cast of molten steel was produced in 1865, after which a full-size Bessemer works was established. The availability of large quantities of steel allowed the construction of larger bridge spans, taller buildings, stronger and lighter machinery, and steel rails for faster trains.

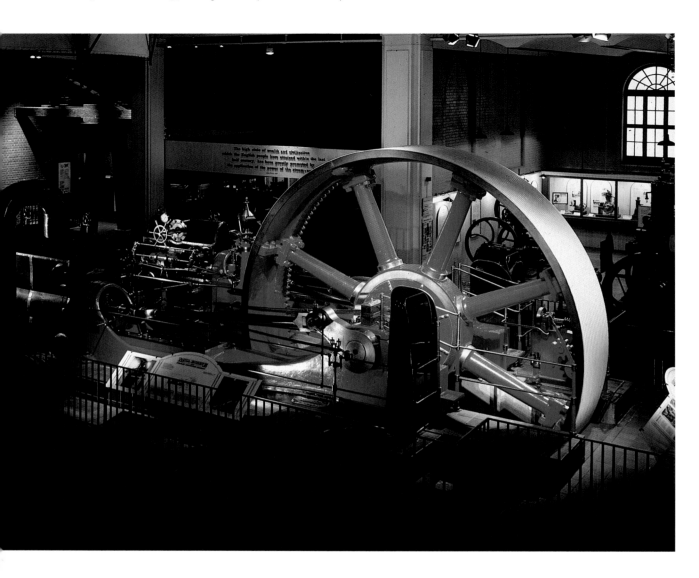

Engine from Harle Syke Mill

The Burnley Ironworks built this engine in 1903 to provide 700 horsepower to Harle Syke Mill. At its peak, the mill housed over 1500 looms weaving cotton cloth. The power from the engine was transmitted to the mill by rope working in the grooves in the wheel. The mill was finally converted to electrical power, making the engine redundant, in 1970.

The Science Museum moved the engine in pieces to its store in 1971. In 1976, Riley & Sons, a firm with long experience of this type of engine, refurbished it and reassembled it in the Museum. A modern boiler was installed later, and the engine was again able to run in 1986. This magnificent engine now runs each day. The huge wheel, as it rotates, is an impressive sight.

The engine is still run on steam, produced in a modern, oil-fired boiler in the Museum basement and piped to the engine. After passing through two cylinders, the steam is mixed with cold water in a condenser (which looks like a third cylinder). This produces a vacuum and the exhaust comes out as lukewarm water.

By adjusting the steam from high boiler pressure down to a vacuum in this way, the engine extracts its energy very efficiently.

For reasons of safety the engine drives nothing and runs at only one-quarter of its intended speed. However, at this speed visitors can better appreciate the wonderful movement of this giant.

Watching the drivers preparing to start the engine, you may witness the long, careful routine of letting steam pass through to warm the engine up before it begins to turn. This is essential, to avoid the risk of water collecting in the pipe work or the cylinder, which could make a hydraulic lock and cause immense damage.

Although the engine weighs about 75 tonnes, the wheel alone weighing 20 tonnes, it is a typical example, of only moderate size. The engine builder anticipated the possibility that more power would be needed if the mill were to be expanded. Each rope would transmit about 50 horsepower, and so the 18 grooves would have allowed for the transmission of up to 900 horsepower. Engines of twice this power were not uncommon, and even bigger ones were built. Besides this, the engineer adopted a robust, conservative design for reliability. The massive wheel helped to ensure even running, which was important because any variation in speed in driving the looms resulted in unevenness in the finished cloth.

Rolls-Royce RB 211

The jet engine was adapted for civil use shortly after the Second World War. The earliest examples were inefficient and noisy. As fuel prices rose, aero-engine manufacturers were under pressure to produce a more fuel-efficient engine. The main principle behind this RB 211 design was an exceptionally large fan designed to drive a large volume of slow-moving air around the core engine, thereby using fuel efficiently and reducing noise. The production of such engines required huge components, high operating temperatures and titanium to make the fan blades. The development proved much more expensive than anticipated, and Rolls-Royce was declared bankrupt. The government took on the costs of development and the RB 211 was finally launched in 1972. The engine became so successful that it ultimately ensured the survival of the company it had originally bankrupted. It has provided the basis for the subsequent development of all other large engines and allowed the new generation of jumbo jet aircraft to take to the air in the early 1970s. The engine shown here was used in a prototype Lockheed TriStar for a total of 28 flights.

Puffing Billy

Puffing Billy is the oldest surviving steam locomotive. Richard Trevithick first adapted the stationary steam engine into a machine capable of replacing horses for the haulage of coal wagons in 1804. This caught the imagination of Christopher Blackett who owned Wylam Colliery in Northumberland. He was interested in replacing horses on the five-mile wagonway which took coal from the colliery to the River Tyne. Blackett decided to build a locomotive able to run on smooth rails to avoid the costly replacement of the cast-iron rails on his wagonway. The colliery manager, William Hedley, thus built *Puffing Billy* around 1814. With two cylinders and a return flue, this engine could pull up to ten coal wagons at speeds of 4–5 mph. *Puffing Billy* continued working at Wylam until 1862, when it was removed to South Kensington.

Boulton and Watt's rotative steam engine

The first steam engines were simply pumping machines, used to extract water from Britain's coal mines. The development of the rotative engine, that would turn a shaft, was an important step forward. This engine, built by James Watt and his business partner Matthew Boulton in 1788, was one of the first rotative engines and has been less altered than any other surviving engine of its age. It was built for Boulton's own works, and initially drove 'lapping' machines for polishing the steel beads which, as dress accessories, were then highly fashionable. The engine worked until 1858. It was moved in 1861 to the Patent Museum, the collections of which were later transferred to the Science Museum. It is arguably the most historic engine in the whole collection, and it stands as a testament to the engineering genius of those who contributed to the huge industrial changes that began in Britain 250 years ago.

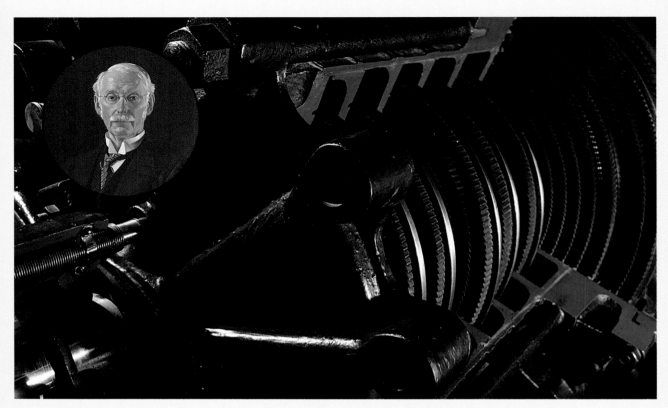

Parsons marine steam turbine

Charles Parsons, while searching for a more efficient steam engine to drive electric generators, began to experiment with turbines in the 1880s. Parsons first applied his turbine to driving generators for electric lighting. After these had proved reliable, Parsons began to develop turbines for marine propulsion, demonstrating his invention using this machine on his launch *Turbinia* in 1894. Steam entered the centre of the engine casing at the shaft and passed radially outwards. The shaft drove a single high-speed propeller. This first marine turbine gave *Turbinia* a speed of 19.75 knots. By 1897 Parsons had developed a turbine in which steam was fed in at one end and passed along the axial length of the unit before leaving at the other end. *Turbinia* was fitted with three such units each taking the same steam at progressively lower pressures, and each driving a separate propeller. The three high-speed propellers enabled *Turbinia* to achieve the then-unprecedented speed of 34.5 knots – a performance which persuaded the Admiralty to adopt steam turbines for the Royal Navy.

Ion engine

A rocket engine operates according to Newton's Third Law of Motion (for every action there is an equal and opposite reaction). The rocket and the vehicle to which it is attached move forward as mass is ejected at high speed in the opposite direction. Conventional rocket engines do this by burning propellant – the heat of the reaction expels the combustion gases. Ion engines, such as this UK 25E example, use an electrical field to accelerate and then expel high-velocity gas ions. The UK 25E engine generates a gentle thrust by extracting and accelerating an ion beam from a plasma of xenon ions created in its discharge chamber. The thrust is small compared to a chemical combustion engine, but its high specific impulse means that it is a highly efficient engine, ideal for powering deep-space missions.

Black Arrow rocket engine

The Black Arrow rocket evolved from the hardware and experience gained during the Black Knight missile project. The single-staged Black Knight test missiles reached altitudes of over 500 km before falling back to Earth when they were tested in Woomera, South Australia, in the 1960s. Two sets of Black Knight's upgraded Gamma 201 engines were later used on the first stage of the Black Arrow rocket, conceived as a small satellite launch vehicle capable of placing a 100 kg payload in a 480 km circular polar orbit. Britain was involved with international rocket launcher programmes, but it was felt that it should develop its own launching capability. However, government support was weak and funding came only in stages, making the development process much slower than expected. Five Black Arrow rockets were built in total. The fourth of these successfully launched the Prospero X-3 satellite into orbit in 1971, but by then the programme had already been cancelled. Britain was the sixth country to launch a satellite using its own rocket. Black Arrow R-4, the fifth vehicle, was never used and is now displayed in the Science Museum.

Bentley rotary engine

During the First World War, the rotary aero-engine was initially the most important type of aircraft power unit on the Allied side. When war broke out, the company Gwynnes, used by the Royal Naval Air Service, employed W O Bentley in their design department to improve the aero-engine concept. Bentley was famous in the 1920s as a racing driver and, although he was successful as an engine-tuner, he had not then designed complete engines. However, his design for the cylinders of the engine shown here was different from other rotary aero-engines in that it used aluminium, a good conductor of heat. This solved the problem of thermal distortion common in other rotary engines. The Bentley engine was built to power fighter planes in the war and was small, compact and powerful, but was replaced by competitive non-rotary aircraft engines after the war.

The first lawnmower

A major social impact of the Industrial Revolution was an increase in the size of the middle classes. Many new houses were built with gardens, so gardening became a popular leisure-time activity. In the eighteenth century, gardeners used scythes to cut lawns. This was a labour-intensive process that often led to irregularities and bare patches of earth being exposed on uneven ground. Edwin Budding invented the first mechanical lawnmower, which had cylindrical shears based on the cutters used for trimming woollen cloth in textile factories. The lawnmower was patented in 1830 as 'a machine for country gentlemen for amusement and exercise'. The company J R and R Ransome were licensed to create the mower, and the attractive example shown here was one of their first machines built in 1832. The mower was pushed from behind and grass could be collected in a flat box attached to the front. Budding's basic design remained unchanged well into the twentieth century and became extremely popular on the tennis courts, cricket grounds and parks that sprang up in the new industrialised society.

Bakelite

Bakelite was the world's first synthetic plastic. It was named after its inventor, the Belgian-born Leo Baekeland, who first developed it in his laboratory near New York and patented it in 1907. Bakelite was a resin produced by a violent reaction between phenol and formaldehyde. Baekeland supplied this resin for use in lead moulds, laminating paper or fabric and for moulding into a variety of products. Bakelite was a very versatile substance, as it was resistant to heat, chemicals and moisture, and had excellent electrical insulation properties. By the late 1920s, it had many practical and decorative uses in homes and industry. Bakelite enabled designers to develop a new range of shapes that could not easily have been made in wood or metal. Brightly coloured objects, such as the radio shown on the right, made of cast phenolic, were popular in the USA. In Britain, people preferred objects that looked like imitation dark wood, such as the television on the right.

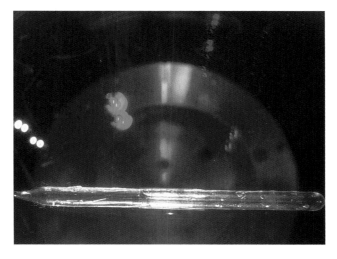

Synthetic ammonia

In the early twentieth century, nearly all the nitrogen compounds used in fertilisers, dyes and explosives came from gasworks or from the Atacama Desert in Chile. Since the supply from gasworks was limited, the world's growing population was becoming increasingly reliant on the British-controlled Chilean nitrate monopoly to supply the fertilisers needed to increase crop yields. The making of synthetic ammonia broke this monopoly and transformed food production for ever. In Germany, just before the First World War, Fritz Haber and Carl Bosch developed a method of synthesising ammonia from nitrogen and hydrogen. By 1916, Germany was producing synthetic ammonia on a large scale for fertilisers and explosives, a vital contribution to its war effort. Ammonia is also used in the production of plastics and dyestuffs. The sample shown here, produced by Haber in 1909, is one of the first synthetic ammonia samples ever made.

Holograms

The Hungarian-born scientist Dennis Gabor (a hologram of whom is shown here) developed the theory of holography in 1947. The first examples were of very poor quality but, after the invention of the laser in 1960, it became possible to produce high-quality holograms. To make a laser hologram, a laser beam is split into two parts, which are expanded by lenses into wide beams. One of the beams shines on to the object, and some of this light is reflected on to a photographic plate. The other beam shines directly on to the photographic plate where it combines with the reflected light to produce the hologram. When another laser beam is shone through the hologram it creates a visible, three-dimensional image. Holograms are fascinating and fun, but also potentially very useful. Most of us are familiar with the holograms found on credit cards, but they have many other uses. There is even a project under way to create holograms of the wreck of *Titanic*.

The V-2 missile

This rocket is the world's first long-range ballistic missile, and is the forerunner of modern space rockets and intercontinental ballistic missiles. It was developed in Germany during the early 1940s by Wernher von Braun and other members of the team who later, in the USA, developed the Saturn V Moon rocket. The V-2 missile was given its name by the Nazi propaganda machine. The German army developed it as a potential weapon of war, its principal targets being London and Antwerp. In October 1942, the first successful launch of an A-4 type V-2 missile took place, hitting its target in the Baltic 192 kilometres away. The V-2 killed many thousands during its deployment in the Second World War, and many also died in the course of its manufacture by slave labour. However, its innovative technology laid the foundations upon which the space rockets of the 1950s and 1960s were built.

Fibre optics

Fibre optics use the ability of light to travel through glass or plastic fibres by total internal reflection. One of the earliest uses for fibre optics was in decorative lighting. 'Mare's tail' lamps contain large numbers of fibres illuminated from a single light source. Fibre optics are also used in endoscopes, such as the one shown here. Endoscopy is the means by which parts of the body such as the lungs, stomach and intestines can be investigated without surgery. By far the biggest use of fibre optics is in the telecommunications industry. For example, optical fibres are used instead of copper wires in telephone cables, and the messages are coded as pulses of light instead of fluctuating electric current.

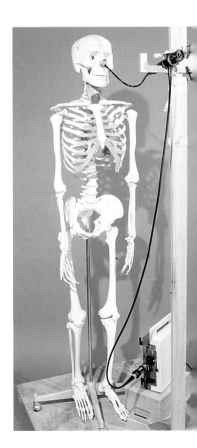

The discovery of penicillin

Alexander Fleming (1881–1955) worked at St Mary's medical school in London, first as a surgeon and then as a bacteriologist. During the First World War, Fleming witnessed the horrific infections suffered by wounded troops. In 1928, while tidying up a pile of Petri dishes in which he had been growing bacteria, Fleming noticed that some mould was growing on one of the dishes, and all the bacteria surrounding it had stopped growing. He examined the mould and discovered it belonged to the penicillium family. Despite his discovery that the mould was exuding a substance which killed certain bacteria, Alexander Fleming did not think of this substance primarily as a medicine. When the German firm IG Farben announced the first general purpose bacteria-killing drug, prontosil, Fleming changed his views. He gave a sample of his mould to a colleague at St Mary's Hospital, after a conversation about prontosil and its possible application to ward off infection. Penicillin was eventually isolated in Oxford in 1939, and from 1942 became an important drug. Alexander Fleming was knighted in 1944 and received a Nobel Prize in 1945. The drugs derived from the mould, collectively named penicillin, were among the first to successfully treat infection in humans. They remain today some of the most important antibiotics.

Alexander Fleming's penicillin sample
Alexander Fleming discovered that a penicillium mould inhibited the growth of certain bacteria. This petri dish originally came from Alexander Fleming himself and is probably one of a number he prepared and used in 1944 to illustrate his 1928 discovery. A secretion from the yellow-coloured mould has stopped the growth of one of the colonies of bacteria on the dish, which appear as streaks on the growth medium.

The discovery of polyethene

Various synthetic materials first appeared in the 1930s, including nylon, polystyrene, PVC and polyethene. Polyethene (better known as polythene) was developed in 1933 and was eventually manufactured in greater quantities than any other plastic. Reginald Gibson and Eric Fawcett, who worked for ICI, first discovered polyethene while using the equipment, part of which is shown here, devised by the Dutch physicist Anton Michels. Michels originally devised apparatus for subjecting material to high pressure as part of a research programe to find new and potentially useful effects of pressure. Gibson and Fawcett set up an experiment in which a mixture of ethylene and benzaldehyde was heated to 170°C under high pressure. They produced a waxy, solid polymer of ethylene, but this result was not successfully repeated until 1937 when Michael Perrin used improved equipment to carry out reproducible polymerisation. Polyethene was first used as an insulating material. Nowadays, it commonly appears in disposable packaging, plastic bags, and many other plastic goods such as pipes, bottles and Tupperware (inset).

EEG cap

The human brain receives and sends millions of electrical messages every day. Doctors can 'tune in' to these messages using electroencephalography (EEG). The 32 electrodes on this EEG cap pick up tiny electrical currents generated by the patient's brain cells. EEG measures electrical activity in the brain via electrodes placed on the patient's skull, and records a wave pattern that varies according to what the person is doing. It can detect electrical changes that happen in a few thousandths of a second. EEG is used to diagnose epilepsy and multiple sclerosis, but it has also been used by volunteers in experiments to see how the brain handles specific tasks such as recognising the wrong words in a sentence.

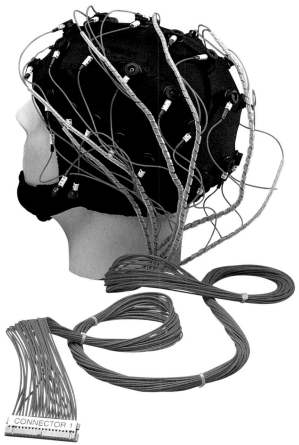

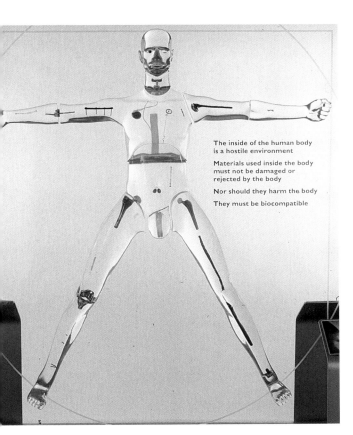

The inside of the human body is a hostile environment

Materials used inside the body must not be damaged or rejected by the body

Nor should they harm the body

They must be biocompatible

Tracy the sheep

Tracy, born in 1990, was a transgenic sheep who could produce protein in her milk for human therapeutic use. Transgenic animals are created when genes, in this case from human DNA, are injected into fertilised embryos. The resulting animal, in a limited number of cases, incorporates the genes into its own DNA. Tracy produced a human protein which it is hoped will prove useful in combating the symptoms of cystic fibrosis.

Polyester resin man

This transparent cast resin body contains visible body parts, showing the materials that surgeons use inside human bodies. These materials are not damaged or rejected by the body and are non-toxic. For example, this model contains an artificial knee made from cobalt alloy, titanium and polyethene. The upper part of the knee is a hardwearing, resistant alloy of cobalt, chromium and molybdenum. The lower part of the knee joint is titanium alloy with a layer of polyethene on top. When the patient bends this artificial knee, the polyethene rubs against the highly polished surface of the cobalt alloy, reducing friction. The resin man also contains polyester vascular grafts, which surgeons use to bypass major arteries that have become blocked. The polyester is often coated in gelatin, so that it becomes water-tight. This gelatin dissolves once inside the body and allows natural tissues to grow onto the graft.

Science

The Museum's collections represent centuries of invention and discovery in science. This section of *Inside the Science Museum* showcases the work of some of the world's greatest scientists. This includes instruments used to observe a range of phenomena, from the solar system to the inside of the human brain. It also includes instruments used to measure quantities from temperature to time. We discuss experiments involving some of the best-known names in the fields of physics, chemistry, biomedicine and mathematics. Finally, detailed coverage of the ever-changing worlds of genetics and computing is provided.

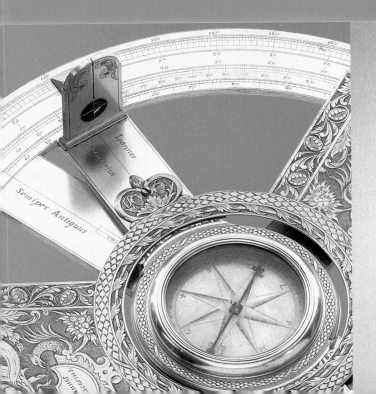

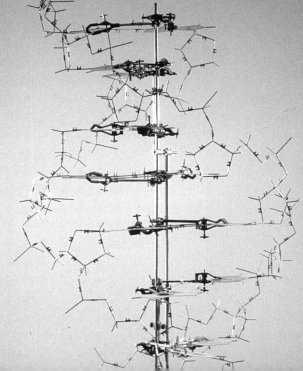

George Adams' silver microscope

In the eighteenth century, science, or 'natural philosophy', was a fashionable pastime among the middle and upper classes. Microscopes, although popular, were seldom used for serious scientific investigation, even though they had been used by men like Robert Hooke in the previous century to carry out important work. In 1761, King George III commissioned apparatus from George Adams to be used by the royal family for entertainment and instruction. These instruments were expensive and elaborate. The tastes of the royal family influenced the fashions of the day, and their patronage was important to Adams. This stunning silver microscope is one of two almost identical models made by George Adams. This one was made for the Prince of Wales, the future George IV; the other was made for George III himself. It is based on Adams' standard microscope design, but is extremely ornate. The instrument, made of brass and steel highly ornamented with silver, stands on an octagonal ebony base.

The first orrery

Today, we accept that the Earth revolves around the Sun and the Moon orbits the Earth. However, before the sixteenth century it was thought that the Earth was the centre of the universe. Nicholas Copernicus first sparked a revolution in human thought by proposing otherwise. The orrery is a planetary machine which shows the planets moving in their orbits around the Sun. Turning a handle moves the spheres that represent the planets. There is a long tradition of constructing models to illustrate the motions of the planets. Between 1704 and 1709, the celebrated clockmaker George Graham made simple planetary machines, showing only the Earth, the Sun and the Moon. Another clockmaker, John Rowley, saw Graham's machines and copied one of them to a commission from Charles Boyle, the fourth Earl of Orrery. This beautiful planetary machine was the first to be called an orrery, named after its purchaser and Rowley's patron. It is thought to have been made around 1712.

J J Lister's microscope

Joseph Jackson (J J) Lister (1786–1869), father of the famous surgeon Joseph Lister, had an abiding interest in microscopy. He devised improved lenses for microscopes, which became serious scientific tools as a result of his work. This important microscope, designed by Lister in 1826, was made by James Smith. It included many improvements on earlier microscopes, but its most significant feature was the superb quality of the objective lens (the one nearest the specimen), made from two different types of glass. Ordinary lenses produced images distorted in shape with coloured fringes around the edges. Lister's 'achromatic' lens suffered much less from these problems. As a result of Lister's developments, accurate observations could be made of muscles, nerves, arteries, cellular membranes and the brain, and the concave disc structure of the red blood cell was revealed. On the strength of his work, Lister was elected a fellow of the Royal Society in 1832.

Caroline Herschel (1750–1848)

Caroline Lucretia Herschel was one of the first women to make a significant contribution to charting the heavens. She was born in Hanover in 1750 where she lived until 1772 when, to escape a difficult home life, she moved to England. Here, she kept house for her brother William, who taught her music and helped her to develop a successful singing career. William became increasingly involved in astronomy and telescope-making, and Caroline began to help him in his astronomical work. In 1781, William discovered a new planet, Uranus, whereupon he was appointed astronomer to King George III. Caroline helped William record his observations by night and carried out the lengthy calculations required to correct his data by day. He made at least two telescopes for Caroline which she used to make her own observations. During the period from 1786 to 1797, she discovered eight comets. She also embarked on an impressive project to correct the errors in the star catalogue produced by John Flamsteed, the first Astronomer Royal, and submitted her work to the Royal Society, with a list of 560 stars previously omitted. Caroline felt displaced after William's marriage but, in later years, she became a great inspiration to her nephew John, William's son, who also became a famous astronomer. Her work continued after she returned to Hanover following William's death in 1822. The Royal Astronomical Society awarded her a gold medal in 1828 for work she did with John. Caroline became one of the first women to be elected honorary member of the Royal Astronomical Society in 1835, together with textbook-author Mary Somerville, and received a gold medal for science from the King of Prussia on her 96th birthday. Caroline died in 1848, having always deflected praise from her own achievements to avoid overshadowing her illustrious brother William.

Christopher Cock's telescope

Christopher Cock belonged to the first generation of optical instrument-makers in London and was one of the two leading names of his time, the other being Richard Reeves. Christopher Cock's ornate terrestrial telescope is the only known surviving instrument signed by him, although he is known to have made, but not signed, Robert Hooke's microscope which is also in the Museum. Making optical instruments in the seventeenth century required great skill, as they were technically demanding and expensively finished. This telescope was made in London in about 1673. It has 'reverse-taper', a common feature of telescopes at this time, which means that the eyepiece is at the larger end. Its body tube is covered in vellum (animal skin) and stamped in gold, with vellum-covered draw tubes and walnut mounts. Three lenses make up the eyepiece, giving a magnification of about 14.

The first brain scanner

This is the first computerised tomography (CT) brain scanner to be installed in a hospital. A conventional X-ray image shows all internal organs superimposed on top of each other, but the CT scanner produces X-ray images of 'slices' across the body, providing far superior diagnostic information. X-ray tomography was invented in the 1920s, but developments in computing, rather than radiology, transformed the technique. Godfrey Hounsfield, the inventor of the scanner, worked for EMI on the development of computer equipment. He devised the hardware and software required to convert X-ray readings, taken from 180 different angles around the head, into an image that could be reconstructed on a monitor. EMI might not have produced the brain scanner in the early 1970s without the profits it made from its music industry. The company had to sell the medical equipment side of its business only eight years after the scanner was first made public, despite the fact that the technique proved highly successful.

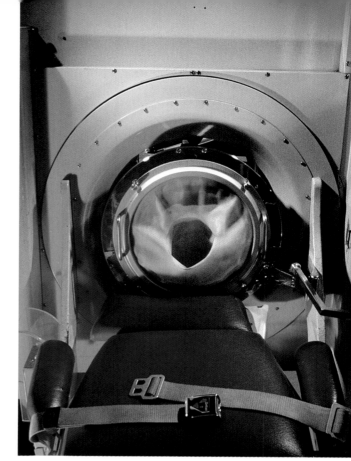

Scanning electron microscope

Using light microscopes we can only view objects that are larger than the wavelength of light (a few ten-thousandths of a millimetre). To see smaller objects electrons are used, because they behave like waves with a much shorter wavelength than light. Electron beams can also be focused by specially designed electromagnets. Max Knoll and Ernst Ruska built the first transmission electron microscope in 1931 in Berlin, in which the electrons pass through the specimen. Charles Oatley and Dennis McMullen built the first successful scanning electron microscope in 1951 in Cambridge. In this instrument the electron beam is scanned across the surface of the specimen. The electrons are scattered back from it and produce an image which appears almost three-dimensional. Scanning electron microscopes were not produced commercially until a number of years later. The machine shown here is one of five produced in a trial by the Cambridge Instrument Company in 1965. By 1985, a thousand instruments a year were being produced, and scanning electron microscopes now outnumber transmission electron microscopes.

Hubble Space Telescope model

The Hubble Space Telescope allows astronomers to see fainter objects and look further into space than ever before. Work began on the telescope in 1977 and it was launched by the space shuttle Discovery on 25 April 1990. Unfortunately, following this launch, the primary mirror was found to be misshapen, which limited its performance. In December 1993, a set of correcting lenses was added to the telescope to remove this defect, in a similar way that spectacles rectify bad eyesight. The telescope assembly is the most precise ever built, with a 2.4m diameter capable of distinguishing the right and left headlights of a car from 4000 km away. Amazingly, the actual design of the telescope is based on one invented in the seventeenth century. The information gathered by the telescope is sent to a tracking and data relay satellite, which beams the observations to a site in New Mexico, USA. A domestic satellite then transmits the information from here to the Goddard Space Flight Centre in Maryland. This model is a 1:5 scale replica, showing the three components making up the telescope: the optical telescope assembly, the scientific instruments and the support systems module. The Hubble telescope will eventually be replaced by the Next Generation Space Telescope. This will build on Hubble's success and help answer some of the most intriguing challenges faced by science. These challenges include defining the nature of black holes, determining if other Earth-like planets exist, and suggesting whether such planets harbour life.

Reynolds' X-ray set

This apparatus is one of the oldest surviving X-ray machines and was used in medical practice. In 1895, Wilhelm Röntgen discovered 'a new type of ray' that was invisible to the eye but could pass through solid objects and affect a photographic plate. Because X-rays passed through flesh more easily than through bone, they could produce shadow pictures showing the bones inside parts of the body. John Reynolds, a London doctor, and his son Russell, saw accounts of the discovery in newspapers early in 1896 and decided to build the X-ray apparatus shown here. Some doctors were quick to show interest in the use of X-rays but it was not until the 1920s that the medical profession began to use X-ray machines widely. Initially they were used mostly to help treat broken bones or to locate bullets and other foreign bodies. Russell Reynolds qualified as a doctor and became an eminent radiologist.

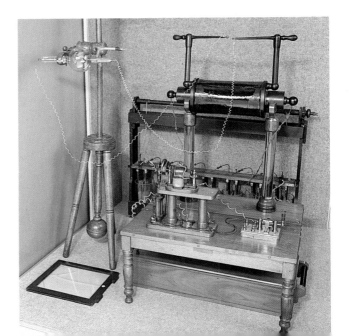

The standards of the realm

In Tudor times, when rapid economic growth occurred in agriculture, commerce and industry, new Exchequer standards of weight, length and capacity were made under Henry VII. More significant advances were made under Elizabeth I, resulting in a set of primary reference standard weights produced for the Exchequer in 1582. These weights, made of bronze engraved with the royal insignia, date from 1582 and 1588 and are a magnificent example of the standards which remained in use until 1824. The troy weights (used to weigh coin or bullion) are a series of nested cups weighing from one-eighth of an ounce to 256 ounces. The avoirdupois standards, used for all other general weighing, are bells or discs weighing from one-16th of an ounce to eight pounds. The Science Museum also displays cast bronze standards of the bushel, gallon, quart and pint from the Elizabeth I era.

Circumferentor

The surveying compass, or circumferentor, was the basic tool of the surveyor and mapmaker. The circumferentor had a magnetic compass fitted with sights so a surveyor could measure angles by recording bearings from one point to another, with reference to the magnetic meridian. Joannes Macarius made this superb example, dated 1676. Circumferentors became very popular for surveying newly-discovered regions. They were also used, in a simpler form, to survey mines.

Astrolabe

Devised about 2000 years ago but only introduced to Europe in the twelfth century, the astrolabe is an astronomical instrument usually made of brass of around 15cm in diameter. It consists of a star map projected onto a flat surface along with a circular scale and sighting device that can be used to measure the altitude and direction of celestial bodies. Together these features allow the user to calculate the time of day or night, and find the time of a celestial event such as a sunrise or sunset. They became one of the basic astronomy teaching tools in the late Middle Ages. Mariner's astrolabes were also used to help with navigation at sea by finding latitude. They consisted of a simple ring marked in degrees with a sighting vane that could be used to measure the altitude of the Sun or stars. This beautiful example dates from 1572. It bears an inscription reading, 'Don Columbinus de Alfiano monacus vallis umbrose utebatur', which means, 'Don Columbinus of Alfiano, a monk at Vallombrosa, used this.'

Ramsden's three-foot theodolite

The first Ordnance Survey maps of Great Britain came about thanks to the Primary Triangulation of Great Britain, a trigonometrical survey initiated by Sir William Roy in 1784. Roy's first task was to fix the relative positions of the observatories of Paris and London more precisely, to create a 'baseline' of known distance. Roy then required an accurate instrument to measure the angles from the baseline to a distant point for the Primary Triangulation, using trigonometry to calculate the distances, or 'lengths' of the other two sides of the triangle. In 1787, Jesse Ramsden, possibly the greatest of English instrument-makers, finished his first theodolite, which could take a bearing on a mark up to 70 miles away with an error in the angle reading of only one 180th of a degree. The instrument shown here is the second theodolite made by Ramsden, a more refined model that was not exceeded in accuracy until the 1930s. Both theodolites were used for the most important of the 229 stations in the Triangulation network. They were extremely precise, thanks to the use of telescopic sights.

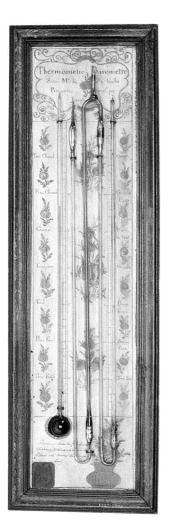

Double barometer by Betali
Barometers and thermometers were invented in the mid-seventeenth century and were in common use in the houses of gentlemen by the eighteenth century. In about 1740 Joseph Betali made this example of a double or folded type, which allows the length of the instrument to be halved. The reading was taken from the right-hand tube, using the level of a light-coloured oil (now evaporated).

Portable sundial
The earliest sundials are from Egypt and date from around 1500 BC. The popularity of the sundial grew, reaching a peak in Europe in Renaissance times. Many new types of dial were made during this period, including portable sundials made of silver, brass, ivory or wood. Some were created by highly skilled mathematical instrument-makers and sold as luxury items to the wealthy. This fine octagonal sundial, in brass, is part of a set of drawing instruments made by Dominicus Lusuerg in Rome in 1701.

The first caesium atomic clock
Modern technologies, especially telecommunications, depend on measuring time very accurately. Atomic clocks provide the highest possible precision. They use the frequency of the radio waves associated with the movement of an atom or molecule from one energy state to another. Dr Louis Essen and Dr Jack Parry at the National Physical Laboratory in Teddington built the first atomic clock using the element caesium. It was completed in 1955 and was accurate to the equivalent of one second in 300 years. Shown here is the caesium beam-tube assembly that was the heart of this clock. The complete system also included several racks of electronics.

Measurements made with this clock provided the essential link between the old, increasingly unsatisfactory, time scales based on astronomical observations and a new atomic time scale. This led, in 1967, to a new definition of the second (the unit of time), in terms of the properties of caesium as used in atomic clocks. International time measurement is now based on this definition. Modern atomic clocks measure time to an accuracy equivalent to one second in millions of years.

Wells Cathedral clock

The second oldest public clock mechanism in Britain can be seen in the Science Museum. It comes from Wells Cathedral, and is believed to be the clock first mentioned in cathedral records from 1392, though it has been altered since then. The steel bells were made for display with the clock in the 1870s. The first public clock recorded in Britain was installed in Salisbury Cathedral in 1386, and still survives there. Clocks like these brought about a change in the way time was measured.

Until the fourteenth century, for civil purposes the periods of daylight and darkness were each commonly divided into 12 'temporal' hours, which varied in length throughout the year. This did not work with mechanical clocks which run at a constant speed, so the system of 24 hours of equal length in a day was adopted gradually during the fifteenth century. Therefore, this fascinating clock played a large part in determining how we measure an aspect of our lives we often take for granted – the passing of time.

Miller's vacuum balance

The use of standard weights and measures to regulate and encourage fair trade has a long tradition. As measurement has improved, standards have been made to far greater accuracy that, in turn, require more precise methods to check them. Designed by W H Miller, this balance was built in 1870 by Oertling for comparing primary and secondary standard weights. This balance is innovative because the weighing process is carried out in a vacuum, a method pioneered by M Deleuil in France. The balance is encased in a thick glass chamber from which the air is removed using a mercury vacuum pump. A system of rods and levers, which use mercury-filled tubes as air seals, allows the weights to be moved to and from the scale pans of the balance.

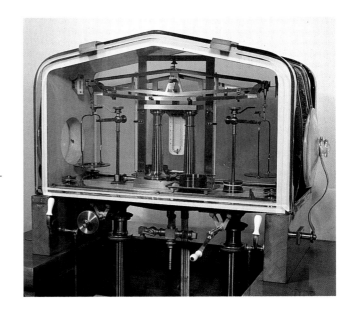

'Forest of rods' model of myoglobin

In the 1930s scientists began to realise that they could better understand the nature of life if they discovered the structure of proteins. In the 1950s at Cambridge University, John Kendrew decoded the structure of myoglobin, a protein which stores oxygen in muscle. Kendrew's first model of myoglobin shows how the single-protein chain folds, enclosing the disc-shaped haem group (the oxygen-binding site). Using X-ray analysis, Kendrew and colleagues produced a series of electron-density maps of myoglobin. From this information, they created a three-dimensional model in 1960, called the 'forest of rods'. The areas of highest electron density (yellow) indicate the protein backbone and haem groups, and the areas of lowest electron density (black) indicate the side chains and spaces. This model provided vital information on how myoglobin functions in the body.

Dorothy Hodgkin's model of insulin

Insulin is a hormone – a chemical messenger – that controls the body's sugar metabolism. Dorothy Hodgkin took the first X-ray diffraction photographs of insulin in 1935. She was sure that the complicated molecular structure of insulin would one day be determined from the diffraction pattern. When she combined her work with that of Fred Sanger, who worked out the order of the protein components – amino acids – that make up insulin, she was able to work out its three-dimensional structure.

This model, which was made around 1967, shows the two chains that together make up insulin. Hodgkin and her co-workers reported the structure of insulin in August 1969. This work was very important for those diabetics who rely on regular doses of insulin to maintain normal sugar levels in their blood. Doctors had given pig insulin to diabetics since the 1920s, but understanding the structure allowed pharmaceutical companies to produce human-type insulin.

Islamic glass alembic

Distillation is one of the oldest chemical processes. The Alexandrian alchemists first developed it *c.* AD 100–900. The process was originally carried out for purifying liquids and preparing medicinal essences. Traditional skills were adopted and developed by Arab chemists, but the apparatus remained essentially the same over time, as indeed it is today. This piece of alchemist's glassware, called an alembic, probably dates from the tenth to the twelfth century. The liquid to be distilled was heated in a lower vessel and the resulting vapour condensed on the inside of the dome shape of the upper vessel – the alembic. The condensed vapour then ran down the internal gutter and out through the spout into a collecting vessel. By the Middle Ages, distillation was used for producing strong acids and alcoholic drinks; in the nineteenth century the process was developed on an industrial scale for the distillation of petroleum. Distillation is still an important technique in the chemical industry.

Molecular model construction kit after A W von Hofmann's pattern

John Dalton, who first formulated atomic theory, was the first to use a type of molecular model in his lectures in 1810. However, before the Karlsruhe Conference of 1860, the structures of even the simplest compounds were uncertain. At this conference, the issue of atomic weights was finally settled – in particular, the atomic weight of carbon was revealed to be 12 rather than six. Chemists now knew how many atoms were found in various molecules. Around this time, several chemists started to put together a theory of chemical structure, from which they could draw the structure of a compound showing how the atoms were connected. Once such structure theory was developed in organic chemistry, atomic theory and molecular models began to be accepted. The Anglo-German chemist August Wilhelm Hofmann began to use molecular models in 1865. As the son of an architect, he saw the models as a form of symbolic architecture. The molecular model construction kit shown here is similar to the ones used by A W Hofmann.

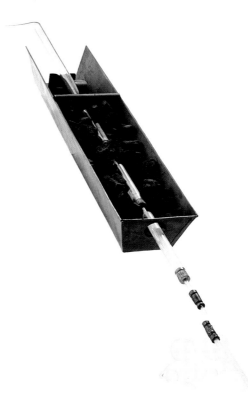

Elemental analysis

The structure of an organic compound is related to the amounts of carbon, hydrogen, nitrogen and oxygen it contains. Justus Liebig introduced a reliable method of determining these amounts in 1837, by using 'combustion analysis', a method which was in use for over a century. During combustion, the compound reacts with oxygen, and the carbon dioxide and water produced in the reaction are collected and weighed. The amount of nitrogen in the compound was originally determined by measuring the nitrogen gas that was liberated when the compound reacted with oxygen or was heated with soda lime. The object shown here is a replica of the 'combustion train' used by Liebig.

Rutherford and the splitting of the atom

Ernest Rutherford was one of the leading nuclear physicists of the twentieth century. Born in New Zealand, Rutherford won a scholarship to Cambridge University in 1895. Here, he carried out postgraduate research under J J Thomson at a very exciting time, which included the discoveries of X-rays, radioactivity and the electron. He later became professor at McGill University in Montreal, Canada, carrying out some of his most important work on radioactivity, the identification of alpha, beta and gamma radiation. In 1907 he moved back to the UK and worked in Manchester on the nature of alpha particles, receiving a Nobel prize for his work. In 1911 Rutherford announced his most revolutionary idea on the nature of the atom. He pioneered the technique of using alpha particles (helium nuclei) from the radioactive decay of thorium to probe other atoms. Hans Geiger and Ernest Marsden, researchers working with Rutherford in Manchester, bombarded gold foil with alpha particles. Most of the particles went straight through, as expected, but a few bounced back as if, in the words of Rutherford, he had: 'fired a 15-inch naval shell at a piece of tissue paper and the shell came right back and hit you'. To explain why a few alpha particles rebounded, Rutherford proposed that the atom is a miniature 'solar system', with a nucleus at its centre and electrons orbiting it. Most alpha particles therefore brushed past the electrons without being deflected, but the few alpha particles approaching the nucleus directly were then deflected by the electric charge on the nucleus. Later Rutherford went further and actually 'split the atom'. Using alpha particles to bombard nitrogen atoms, he detected nuclei of hydrogen that appeared to have been 'chipped off' the nitrogen nuclei. In 1920 he speculated that these hydrogen nuclei were the building blocks of all nuclei, and suggested the name 'proton' for this unit. This model of the atom eventually gained general acceptance. Rutherford also predicted the existence of neutrons, which were later discovered by James Chadwick. From 1919 until his death in 1937 Rutherford was head of the Cavendish Laboratory in Cambridge, turning it into a world leader in nuclear physics.

Geissler tube

Since the early eighteenth century it had been known that, if an electric current is passed through a gas at a pressure much lower than that of the atmosphere, it makes the gas glow. In 1855, Heinrich Geissler, a glassblower in Bonn, devised a new pump that produced a much better vacuum than ever before. He used the pump to evacuate intricately shaped glass tubes to demonstrate this colourful electrical effect. These tubes, such as the one shown here, became known as Geissler tubes. Geissler also made tubes for use in research. A scientist called Julius Plücker discovered cathode rays using tubes made by Geissler. William Crookes used a pump developed from Geissler's to evacuate the tubes he made for his important experiments on cathode rays.

Cockcroft and Walton's accelerator

This accelerator, built by John Cockcroft and Ernest Walton at the Cavendish Laboratory in Cambridge in 1932, was the first to be used to 'split the atom'. Protons, the nuclei of hydrogen atoms, are released at the top of a glass column which has been emptied of air. The protons, which are positively charged, pass through a series of electrically charged metal cylinders, which accelerates the protons. The target material is placed in the path of the protons at the far end of the glass tube. Cockcroft and Walton first used their accelerator to bombard lithium atoms, splitting them to produce helium nuclei. They were awarded the Nobel prize for physics in 1951 for this work. Previously, experiments on the nucleus had used radioactive materials as a source of particles for bombarding nuclei, but such methods were expensive and produced unreliable results. The principle of the Cockcroft and Walton machine is still used today in the first stage of the largest accelerators.

Crookes' cathode ray tube

William Crookes, the British chemist and physicist, is known for many things including his discovery of the element thallium, his radiometer, and his cathode-ray research which was fundamental in the development of atomic physics. In 1878 he published a detailed account of the properties of cathode rays which he investigated using what became known as 'Crooke's tubes', made in his own laboratory. These were sealed glass tubes containing two metal electrodes, and almost completely emptied of air. When a high voltage was applied to the two electrodes, cathode rays were produced at the negative electrode, or cathode, and travelled across the tube creating a glow where they struck the glass. Crookes showed that cathode rays could cast a shadow on a piece of metal placed in their path, proving that they travel in a straight line. His experiments were a step on the way to a number of extremely important discoveries, such as X-rays and electrons. The Crookes tube led to the modern cathode ray tube, used in television sets, computer terminals, radar sets and other measuring instruments.

Bell jar and pump

The air pump was one of the new types of instrument used in the seventeenth century by members of the Royal Society interested in natural philosophy. Investigators used air pumps to examine the various properties of air. Two eminent members of the Royal Society, Robert Boyle and Robert Hooke, reported experiments using air pumps, including the effects of placing burning candles or small animals in a glass vessel on top of the apparatus and removing air from it. Francis Hauksbee, who was appointed Curator of Experiments at the Royal Society by Sir Isaac Newton, built this very fine and decorative example of an air pump in 1705. When the air was removed from the bell jar by the air pump, the bell became inaudible, since sound does not travel through a vacuum.

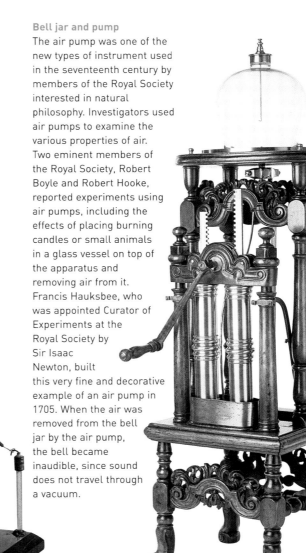

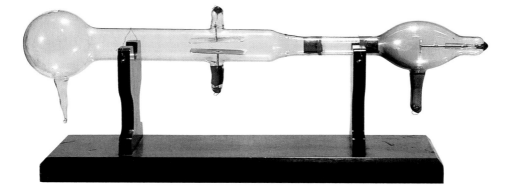

Thomson's discovery of the electron

Shown here is one of the original vacuum tubes used in the ground-breaking experiments of J J Thomson at the Cavendish Laboratory of Cambridge University, which led him to propose the existence of the electron in 1897. Thomson believed that cathode rays were streams of particles, not electromagnetic radiation as many other scientists thought. He used tubes like this to measure the ratio of the electric charge to the mass of these particles. His measurements led him to suggest that the particles, now known as electrons, were much lighter than even the hydrogen atom, the lightest particle known until then. Thomson's discovery was one of the most important in physics at the end of the nineteenth century, pointing the way to modern atomic and nuclear physics.

Chadwick's paraffin wax

James Chadwick is celebrated for establishing the existence of
neutrons, the particles found alongside protons in the nuclei of
atoms. Chadwick's work was influenced by ideas proposed by
Ernest Rutherford, who speculated that positively
charged protons in the nucleus might be
accompanied by other units with no
electric charge – neutrons. No light was
shed on these mysterious particles, until, in
the 1930s, physicists in Germany, France
and Britain used alpha particles (helium
nuclei) to bombard material such as
beryllium. Chadwick carried out his own
experiments along these lines, putting the
pieces of paraffin wax shown here in the way of
the radiation produced by beryllium. The
radiation knocked hydrogen nuclei (protons) out
of the wax but, when Chadwick repeated the
experiment, his calculations led him to conclude
that particles with the same mass as protons but
which were electrically neutral had also been
knocked out. This neutral particle was, he thought,
the neutron proposed by Rutherford. Chadwick
underestimated the effect his findings would have.
Towards the end of the 1930s, scientists discovered
that neutrons could split uranium nuclei, releasing
large amounts of energy. Within 13 years of Chadwick's
discovery, neutrons had made possible the development of
atomic bombs and nuclear reactors. The neutron therefore led to
some dramatic changes in a very short time.

Lawrence's 11-inch cyclotron

Ernest Lawrence began studying atomic nuclei at the
University of California, Berkeley, in 1928. He knew that
the only way to investigate a nucleus closely was to
bombard it with other nuclei, such as hydrogen nuclei
(protons) accelerated to high energies so they could
penetrate the target nuclei. However, the several hundred
thousand volts of electricity required to do this could cause
serious electrical breakdown. Lawrence's ingenious
solution to this problem was that, instead of being
accelerated in a straight line, the particles could be
whirled round in a spiral motion, and gradually gain energy
as a result. He developed his first working 'cyclotron', with
his student Stanley Livingston, in 1931 for this purpose. A
voltage, applied across the gap between two magnets
housed in D-shaped cavities in the cyclotron, accelerated
particles as they passed back and forth. Lawrence was
awarded the Nobel prize for physics in 1939 and, thanks to
him, cyclotrons are used to this day to probe the
structure of matter and produce radioactive
materials for the treatment of cancer.
Unfortunately, he lost the race to split the atom to his
competitors, Cockcroft and Walton (p. 36).

Joule's paddle-wheel apparatus

James Prescott Joule performed a series of experiments in the 1830s which showed that heat was produced by an electric current. Until then it had been mistakenly believed that heat was conserved and transferred rather than created, so Joule's ideas were not accepted at first. However, he was undaunted. He built the apparatus shown here, in which mechanical work (one form of energy) was converted directly into heat (another form of energy) by stirring water vigorously with a horizontally rotating paddle wheel. In 1847, his ideas attracted the attention of William Thomson (later Lord Kelvin). Joule's work led Thomson and others to develop the theory of thermodynamics, which states that one form of energy can be converted into another. Joule's research led to the unit of measurement for all energy being called the joule.

Model of a nuclear reactor

This model is based on the advanced gas-cooled reactor (AGR) at Heysham 2, near Morecambe in Lancashire. It is a life-size replica of part of the AGR , showing the top of the graphite core of the reactor. The circular channels in the graphite core contain the fuel. When it is operating, the reactor is filled with carbon dioxide gas at a very high temperature (more than 600 °C) and pressure (over 40 atmospheres). This gas, or 'coolant', carries the heat from the fuel to the boilers on the left where it is used to turn water into steam. In turn, the steam spins a turbo-generator to produce electricity.

Cascade generator

In 1932, John Cockcroft and Ernest Walton devised a technique for bombarding atomic nuclei with protons accelerated in a powerful electric field. This enabled them to explore theories about the basic composition of matter by 'splitting the atom'. This machine is the cascade generator, built by Philips of Eindhoven in 1937. It was designed to produce the high voltage required (up to 1.25 million volts) to accelerate protons. During the Second World War, the machine was used to investigate the properties of uranium and plutonium, work which contributed to the Manhattan Project to manufacture the first atomic bombs.

Crick and Watson's DNA model

In 1951, James Watson and Francis Crick, working in the Cavendish Laboratory of Cambridge University, were determined to discover the structure of DNA. Thanks to X-ray diffraction images, they knew that the atoms were arranged in a regular way. The diffraction patterns obtained from DNA fibres by Rosalind Franklin and Maurice Wilkins at Kings College London revealed a cross shape. Also, Crick had previously demonstrated mathematically that diffraction patterns of a helix (a spiral shape) took the form of a cross. Crick and Watson started to build a model structure that fitted in with this data. In 1952, Rosalind Franklin produced more pictures of DNA that showed it contained two chains. Crick and Watson knew that these long chains were made up of alternating sugar and phosphate groups, and Erwin Chargaff had discovered that four possible bases, each existing as a pair with weak bonds, could be attached to the sugar groups. Watson realised that the shape of each pair meant that the bases could fit down the centre of a double helix formed by the two backbone chains. Crick and Watson, together with Maurice Wilkins, thus built their double-helix model in 1953, using the metal plates shown here. They won a Nobel prize in 1962 for this crucial work.

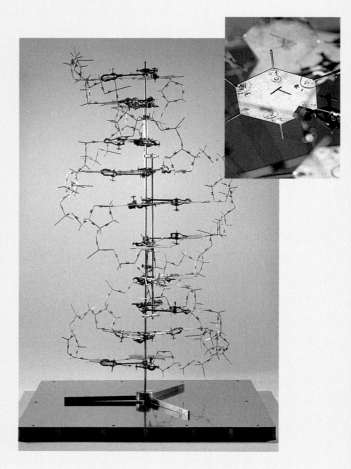

DNA synthesiser, c. 1980

DNA synthesisers are essential devices in biotechnology laboratories, and have been used as a component in work ranging from genetic modification of foods to animal cloning and genetic fingerprinting. These procedures often entailed the building of short stretches of synthetic DNA. This machine is an early automated DNA synthesiser, which could greatly speed up the complex task of DNA synthesis.

Jumper knitted from wool of Dolly the sheep

The first successful cloning of an adult mammal, which produced Dolly the sheep, received enormous media attention when it was announced in February 1997. This work was carried out at the Roslin Institute, a government research facility near Edinburgh. Keith Campbell and Ian Wilmut cloned an adult ewe using a process called nuclear transfer. They replaced the DNA-containing nucleus of an egg cell with the nucleus of an adult ewe udder cell, containing the entire DNA of the donor sheep. The reconstructed egg was then implanted into a surrogate mother sheep, which gave birth to Dolly. The researchers wanted to establish improved methods for genetically modifying livestock. This issue has become very emotive, but cloning also has many applications in medicine, including the production of human hormones such as insulin, organ transplantation and the understanding of ageing and disease. Barry Greenwood at the University of Leeds knitted this jumper from Dolly's first fleece, to a design by 12-year-old Holly Wharton. Holly won a nationwide competition organised by the Science Museum, the Cystic Fibrosis Trust and Portman Building Society.

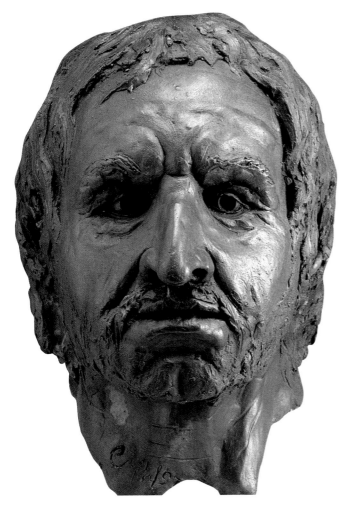

Bleadon Man facial reconstruction

Geneticists studied the 2000-year-old skeleton of a man found in Bleadon, Somerset, and identified four of his relatives living in the village. They found that these people all had the same sequence of DNA in their mitochondrial DNA (mtDNA) as Bleadon Man. MtDNA is passed down the generations in the female line from mothers to their children. Caroline Wilkinson at Manchester University made the reconstruction of what Bleadon Man's face may have looked like. She used well-established information plus her knowledge of facial muscle and soft tissue.

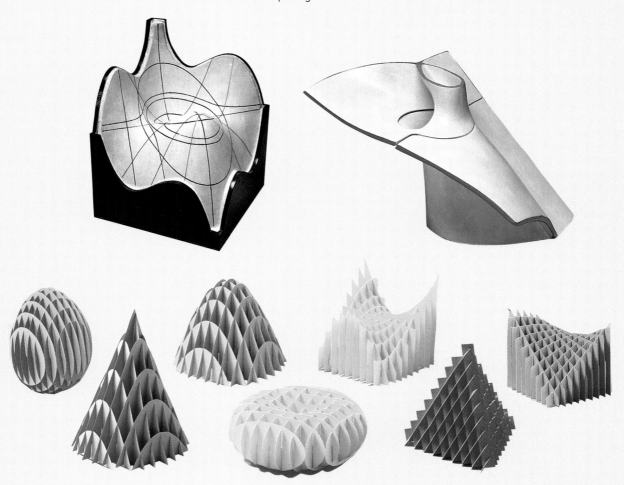

Surface models

During the nineteenth century, mathematics experienced a revival in geometric ideas. Students studying military architecture and engineering used models in lessons on descriptive geometry. From the 1860s onwards, hundreds of models were made to illustrate many areas of the subject. The largest and most innovative workshop was in Munich, where Felix Klein and Alexander von Brill reached 'the furthest frontiers of research' with their mathematical models made from clay, cardboard and string. The models were sold to universities all over Europe. After the First World War, changes in the direction of mathematics, together with general economic upheaval, brought an end to surface model building on a grand scale. The cardboard slice forms (bottom) were made by John Sharp in 1998 using similar techniques to those of Alexander von Brill. The white plaster models by Alexander Crum (top), a professor of mathematics at Edinburgh, were made in 1900 and form part of a collection in the Science Museum.

Uniform polyhedra

In geometry, a solid figure with four or more plane faces, each of which is a polygon, is known as a polyhedron. Knowledge of the properties of polyhedra is needed in crystallography and stereochemistry to determine the shapes of crystals and molecules. There are 76 types of uniform polyhedra in total, but only nine of them are regular polyhedra (with all faces the same size and shape). Five of these were deduced by early Greek mathematicians, and are known as the 'platonic solids': the tetrahedron (four equilateral triangle faces), the cube (six square faces), the octahedron (eight equilateral triangles), the dodecahedron (12 regular pentagons) and the icosahedron (20 equilateral triangles). More complicated are the star polyhedra discovered by Johannes Kepler in 1619. Each star polyhedron has 12 star-shaped faces, which intersect one another. Shown here are a selection of uniform polyhedra from the Science Museum collection.

Charles Babbage's inventions

In 1821, Charles Babbage, dismayed at the number of errors in printed mathematical tables, launched himself on a grand venture to build accurate mechanical calculating engines. During the 1820s, he designed his Difference Engine No. 1, a vast machine requiring some 25,000 parts. The whole machine was never built, though one-seventh of it was assembled by the engineer Joseph Clement in 1832. This finished portion of the unfinished engine is operated by cranking a handle and is the first known automatic calculator in existence. In 1834, Babbage conceived his Analytical Engine. The design of this machine embodies almost all the main logical features of the modern digital computer, the principles of which were reinvented by electronic engineers in the 1940s. Babbage's Analytical Engine was programmable using punched cards and had separate sections for memory and processing. Babbage is widely regarded as the first pioneer of computing, largely because of the Analytical Engine. This engine was never built, though a small experimental section (shown here) was under construction at the time of his death in 1871.

Pilot ACE

The Pilot ACE (Automatic Computing Engine) is the oldest complete general-purpose electronic computer in Britain. Pilot ACE was designed and built between 1949 and 1950 at the National Physical Laboratory at Teddington in Middlesex. The design derives from the work of Alan Turing, the wartime mathematician and code-breaker, who worked at the NPL between 1945 and 1947. Construction started in early 1949 and, in late November 1950, a three-day press demonstration was held. During the demonstration reporters tried to beat the machine in recognising a six-figure prime number. The computer worked faultlessly throughout the demonstration but failed straight afterwards for several weeks. The machine was repaired and upgraded and, in June 1951, it printed out the solution to 17 simultaneous equations after a few hours of computation. In the 1950s, Pilot ACE was used to calculate bomb trajectories, aircraft wing flutter and to test crystallography theory. It remained in service until it was presented to the Science Museum in 1956. Pilot ACE's first public demonstration is shown here.

Society

The technological and scientific developments covered in the previous two sections have had a huge impact on our society. We have chosen some of the objects that best represent these changes for this section of *Inside the Science Museum*. Developments in medicine are recorded in the vast range of drugs and equipment shown, from basic implements to sophisticated diagnostic machines. We also feature innovations in road, rail, air and space travel. Some of the significant developments in the agricultural industry are outlined, and there is a brief look at how communication has changed over the years. This section concludes with some of the inventions that have affected the workplace, improved conditions in the home or increased our scope for leisure.

David Livingstone's medicine chest

David Livingstone was a missionary and explorer, as well as a qualified doctor, who travelled 29,000 miles (46,660 km) throughout Africa. He discovered the Zambesi River, was the first European to see the Victoria Falls and was probably the first individual to traverse the entire length of Lake Tanganyika. Livingstone landed in Africa in 1841 and, for 16 years, worked for the London Missionary Society, teaching, preaching and treating illnesses with his British medicines. In 1858, he was employed by the British government as the Consul for the East Coast of Africa and accepted the challenge of exploring the eastern and central portions of the African continent. This chest dates from around 1860, and was probably used on Livingstone's last expedition through Africa, from 1866 to 1873. It is remarkably well-preserved and contains, among other drugs, a bottle of concentrated ammonia solution for snake bites.

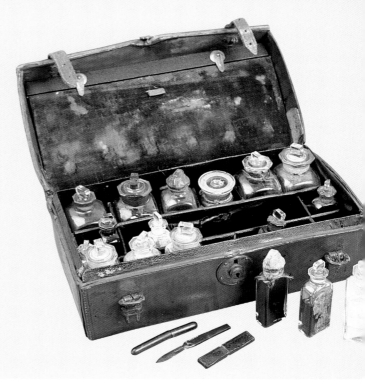

Egyptian amulets

The Egyptians believed in supernatural as well as natural causes of illness. Their methods of disease prevention and treatment therefore involved prayers to the gods, magical incantations and the use of amulets. Amulets were also used to protect the mummified bodies of the dead. Ancient Egyptian amulets often represent a particular deity, one of their attributes or an animal associated with them. Other amulets represent parts of the body, such as the heart (which was considered to be the seat of the mind and emotions), or the backbone (which was a symbol of fortitude). Amulets of the backbone, or *djed* as they were known, were often placed on a mummy to give qualities of strength and stability to the dead. Eye amulets, such as those shown here, conferred good health and general well-being. They are thought to have represented the eye of the Sun or Moon, or it is possible they were designed to protect against the Evil Eye.

Leech jar

Leeches are blood-sucking, aquatic, parasitic, segmented worms. They have been used from as far back as the second century BC as a means of drawing blood locally and controllably from patients by applying them to various parts of the body. They were particularly popular in the eighteenth century. Medical practitioners kept leeches in containers of water, covered with gauze or muslin, in a dark room. Pharmacists often put the day's fresh supply in decorative jars, such as this early nineteenth-century example. The jar has a bell-shaped lid perforated with air holes. Considering its purpose, this jar is a remarkably attractive object, decorated with blue marbling and gilt.

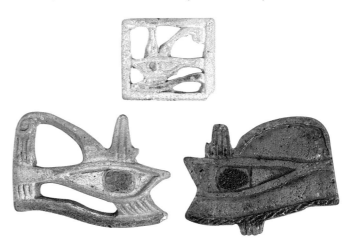

Operations in 1895 and 1980
The top right reconstruction represents the scene of a typical operation in 1895. The surgeons used instruments treated with carbolic acid to kill germs. The patient was anaesthetised with ether or chloroform dropped onto gauze held over the face. The surgeons washed their hands and wore special coats, but did not use gloves or masks, and students in ordinary clothes could watch the operation from nearby. At this time, it was not possible to give successful blood transfusions. Only a small range of operations could take place. In contrast, the centre right reconstruction represents the scene of an open-heart operation from 1980. The operating theatre is full of equipment for monitoring the patient's condition while under anaesthetic, and for keeping the patient alive while the heart is stopped to allow an artificial valve to be sewn in. All the equipment on the site of the operation is completely sterile, including every single small instrument, and a large team is on hand to make sure the procedure goes to plan. Thanks to new surgical machinery, blood transfusions and ways of preventing infection, patients can now survive complicated operations, whereas 150 years ago operations were dangerous enough to be undertaken only in the most serious of cases.

Giustiniani medicine chest
This huge, magnificent medicine chest is solidly constructed from partly gilded wood, with a leather covering and a classical landscape painting inside the lid. There are 126 drugs, bottles and pots stored in the upper compartment and three velvet-lined lower drawers. The chest dates from the 1560s. Ninety-five containers in the chest have labels, apparently handwritten in the sixteenth century, which reveal contents including guaiacum, used as a remedy for syphilis. The Giustiniani chest's elaborate design and array of medicines probably indicates that it was privately owned and used by the wealthy Giustiniani family (Vincenzo Giustiniani was the last Genoese ruler of the Aegean island of Chios). The family probably took the chest with them everywhere, even on sea voyages.

Moreen Lewis's kidney machine

Moreen Lewis was one of the first patients in Britain to have a kidney machine in her home. In the 1960s, doctors disagreed about whether patients should be given their dialysis treatment at home. Home dialysis disrupted the patient's domestic life severely. Structural alterations to the house might be needed. The patient had to spend long hours attached to the machine, and often worried about it breaking down. Moreen Lewis relied on this machine for nine years. She had to find £7000 to pay for it, as the National Health Service at this time only supplied dialysis for acute kidney failure.

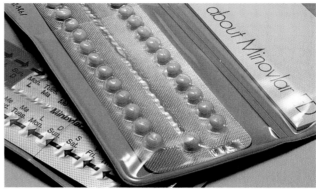

Vaccination kits

Two of the three vaccination instruments shown below were made and used nearly two centuries apart. They show how medical practice can occasionally come almost full circle. When Edward Jenner carried out his first vaccination in 1796, he used a simple blood-letting lancet (bottom left). After the Vaccination Act 1853, many people developed different and complex types of vaccinator. During the ultimately successful campaign to eradicate smallpox in the 1960s and 1970s, various types of vaccine 'gun', some of which forced the vaccine through the skin without a needle, were tried (bottom middle). In the end, however, one of the most popular instruments in the field was the very simple bifurcated needle (bottom right). A drop of vaccine held between the needle's tines entered the skin via the puncture made by its sharp tips, proving that, even in medicine, the appropriate technology is often the simplest.

The contraceptive pill

In the 1920s, scientists were studying sex hormones, taken in small amounts from animals. In 1942, an American chemist found that a hormone, very similar to the female hormone progesterone, could be made from extracts of the Mexican yam. Bulk supplies of this hormone became available once this cheap source was discovered. Ten years later the hormone was available as a medicine in the USA. The birth control campaigner Margaret Sanger raised money for scientists to work on a contraceptive pill containing the progesterone-like hormone. The first oral contraceptive was marketed in the USA in 1960. In Britain, the pill was available only to married women until 1967. By 1970, it was available to all women on the National Health Service. Over 60 million women worldwide now take the pill, which has contributed to the changing role of women in society. It is now available in two forms: the combined pill, which contains synthetic hormones similar to progesterone and oestrogen, and the 'minipill', which contains progesterone only.

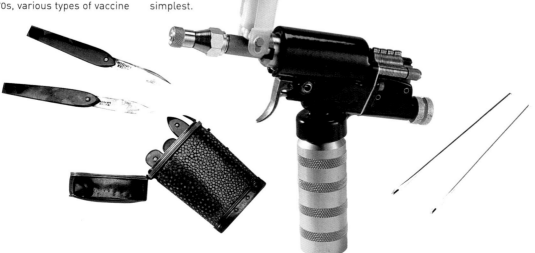

Mobile X-ray machine

X-ray machines were the earliest medical machines to become common in hospitals. However, they were still rare before the First World War. The skill of examining patients using only simple instruments such as the stethoscope was highly prized. Some doctors thought it was almost 'cheating' to make a diagnosis from an X-ray produced by a machine. Many doctors became familiar with the use of X-rays during military service. By the 1930s, hospitals were increasingly using mobile machines, like this one, for patients who were too ill to be moved to an X-ray room. By the 1940s, hospitals such as St Bartholomews in London were taking 500 X-rays per week.

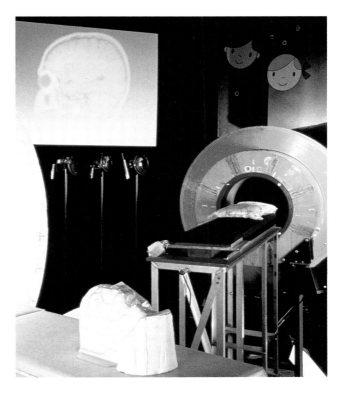

MRI scanner

Dramatic new pictures of the inside of the body were first produced in the 1970s by computerised tomography (CT) scanning, then by magnetic resonance imaging (MRI). Non-medical scientists devised both of these techniques in science and engineering laboratories. Unlike CT scanning, which uses X-rays, MRI uses giant magnets combined with radio waves to create an image. Placing small radio receiver coils directly on the part of the body being examined improves the image. These coils (below), from Hammersmith Hospital in London, are mounted on bicycle helmets. They were called 'Jedi helmets'. It was hoped that, if the helmets were named after the Jedi Knights from the *Star Wars* films, children needing brain scans would be made less anxious about wearing them.

Amy Johnson's aeroplane

Amy Johnson made the first solo flight from England to Australia by a woman. She had only had 61 hours of solo flying by the time she took off from Croydon aerodrome in her Gipsy Moth, *Jason*, in May 1930. She had trained as a ground engineer so that she could carry out any maintenance on the 10,000 mile (16,000 km) trip. The flight was not all smooth going – Amy was forced to land in a blinding sandstorm in Baghdad, and also crash-landed in a ditch on the edge of a football pitch in Rangoon. When she arrived in Darwin, she had become a celebrity. She later admitted that she was not frightened before she set off simply because she had no idea what she had taken on. Johnson's flying career continued throughout the 1930s, but in 1941 she tragically died in an accident while on a wartime aircraft-delivery flight in bad weather. De Havilland Gipsy Moth aeroplanes made a major contribution to the growth of private and sport flying between the world wars. About a thousand of them were built at Edgware and were used in flying clubs and schools throughout Britain.

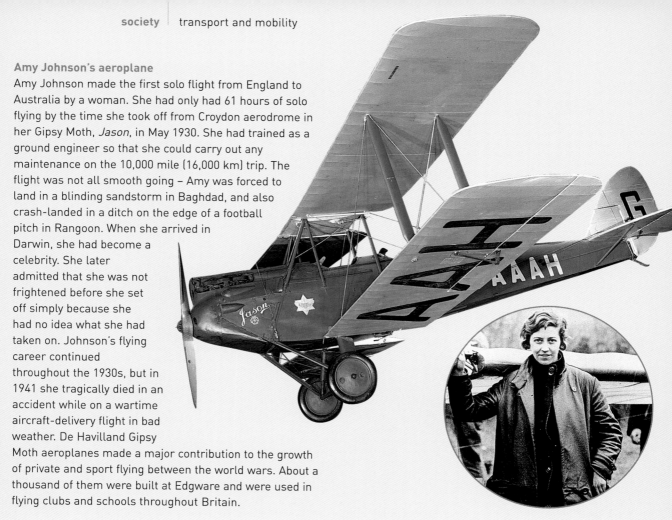

Apollo 10

The Apollo programme was one of the most expensive and ambitious peacetime projects ever undertaken. In May 1961, President John Kennedy initiated the project at the height of the Cold War. He wanted to demonstrate to the world that the democratic capitalism of the West, as exemplified by the USA, was superior to the totalitarian communism of eastern Europe, as exemplified by the Soviet Union. This Apollo 10 command module carried astronauts Tom Stafford, John Young and Gene Cernan around the Moon in May 1969, during the final rehearsal mission for the landing of Apollo 11 in July. The command module was attached at its base to the cylindrical service module, which contained instrumentation and supplies. The other end of the command module docked with the lunar module to provide access between the two spacecraft. During re-entry into the Earth's atmosphere, the convex base of the command module provided some aerodynamic control and burned away by several centimetres to dissipate the 3000 °C heat build-up. The astronauts eventually landed in the ocean in this capsule at the end of their voyage. The images of the Earth captured by the astronauts on the Apollo mission are a lasting legacy of their achievement, and have helped open our eyes to the fragility of our planet.

Rover safety bicycle

In the early 1870s, the Ordinary, or penny-farthing, bicycle was very popular, even though its large front wheel made it unstable, unsafe and tiring to operate. The availability of better materials and technology, such as chains, in the 1880s led to the production of the 'safety bicycle', so named because of its increased stability and reduced height. John Kemp Starley set up his own bicycle manufacturing business in Coventry, which eventually became the Rover Company Limited. Cycle production continued there until 1926. The bicycle shown here was originally designed and introduced by Starley and Sutton in 1885. Its diamond-shaped frame gives structural strength while remaining light and compact. It set the trend for future technical development and commercial production. Many improvements were made in later years to produce the comfortable, safe bicycles on sale today.

Mad Dog 2, 1998

This is Britain's most successful solar-powered racing car, developed by a team at South Bank University and built in 1998. Its aerodynamic design minimises air resistance and it is powered by BP silicon monocrystalline solar cells. In 1998, the car took part in the World Solar Rally in Japan and came first in the Stock class, achieving a speed of 40 km/h. The ultimate goal of the Mad Dog project is to create the 'Millennium Car', a prototype solar-powered family car to investigate the viability of a sustainable-energy vehicle. The Mad Dog cars have appeared at numerous events throughout the world, thereby raising public awareness of the possibilities of solar energy.

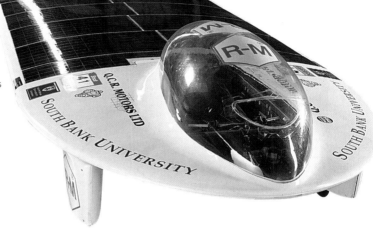

Stephenson's *Rocket*

Rocket marks one of the key advances in railway technology. It also confirmed its designer Robert Stephenson as one of the premier engineers of his age. Robert Stephenson & Co. built the locomotive in 1829 at their works in Newcastle-upon-Tyne as an entrant in the Rainhill Trials, held by the new Liverpool & Manchester Railway to choose between competing designs. The performance of *Rocket* at Rainhill, where it achieved a speed of 29 mph (47 km/h), showed it to be the most successful of the contestants. It also convinced the railway company that the alternative possibility of using stationary steam engines to haul carriages by cables was not worth pursuing. *Rocket* established the basic architecture for the steam locomotive, bringing together several crucial innovations such as the multi-tubular boiler, the blast pipe and direct drive from piston to wheel. It was soon rebuilt to incorporate further modifications, losing its familiar 'Rainhill' appearance in the process, but *Rocket* has survived to become one of the most important symbols of our transport history.

Diorama of medieval ploughing

The scene depicted in this diorama is based on illustrations in the fourteenth-century Luttrell Psalter in the British Museum, London. The scene shows how, in Medieval times, arable land was laid out in huge, open fields. This arrangement was ideally suited to the long, mouldboard ploughs used at this time. Each farmer was allocated a strip of land, typically 201 x 20 metres. The strips were allocated in rotation so that sowing could be done progressively. By the end of autumn, each farmer could have a total of five acres of crops, such as corn, in several different strips. Farmers communally owned and drove the oxen and ploughs. Other operations, such as harrowing and weeding, were the responsibility of each individual. The ploughs tended to tear up the earth, rather than producing a neat furrow, so other workers had to go through the fields 'clod crushing' to break up the soil. This scene also shows men and women harvesting with sickles, weed burning and carting corn in a Saxon cart.

Kent plough

The Kent plough, which is believed to have originated in northern France, is the oldest type of 'turnwrest' plough used in the UK. The plough is so named because the wrest (mouldboard), which pushes the lifted slice of soil over, could be 'turned', i.e. detached from one side of the plough and remounted on the other. This was done at the end of each furrow so that the soil was laid the same way in each direction. This plough is mentioned in writings from the sixteenth century, but never in a very positive light – most writers were scornful of its clumsiness and heaviness. Despite these disadvantages, the Kent plough was actually ideal for the chalky hills and absorbent lowlands of Kent, Surrey and West Sussex. Farmers in these areas continued to use it throughout the centuries, ignoring the many improvements in plough design that took place. By removing the wrest and fitting a broadshare in place of the narrower share normally used, the plough could be used as an excellent skim or sub-plough, capable of clearing stubble from fields. This particular example was built around 1850.

Bell's reaper

Until the early nineteenth century, reaping, or the cutting of corn at harvest, required hand-held sickles and scythes and was very labour intensive. Many attempts at designing a mechanical reaper were unsuccessful until Patrick Bell, a farmer's son, designed this reaper. His design incorporated the cutting action of garden shears and was meant to ease the heavy workload put upon his father's workers at harvest time. The reaper was successfully exhibited at a few venues in 1828, but interest was slow to develop. The reapers required heavy maintenance, which meant that many fell into disrepair. It was not until the Great Exhibition of 1851 that Bell achieved recognition for an improved reaper that was powered by two horses and had a better cutting mechanism. In 1867, two years before he died, Bell received a testimonial and £1000 from the Highland and Agricultural Society of Scotland in appreciation of his work.

Ferguson tractor and plough, 1935

This tractor was built in 1933 in Belfast and is probably one of the most important ever built. It is the prototype model with which Harry Ferguson developed the principles of three-point linkage, hydraulic weight transference and automatic depth control of mounted implements. This enables the implement (a plough, for example) to 'float' behind the tractor so that its depth is automatically maintained even when the tractor wheels drop into hollows in the ground, or the tractor itself rides over an abnormal obstruction. More than any other single development, this package of inventions and its associated 'family' of implements revolutionised the use of the farm tractor. Nearly all subsequent tractor designs have incorporated these principles, making this machine one of the icons of agricultural history.

Massey-Ferguson combine harvester

The combine harvester is a self-propelled machine, which cuts, gathers and clears dried seed and leguminous crops. (Nowadays specialised pea viners and bean harvesters cut peas and beans fresh for frozen-food factories.) The combine harvester is divided into three main units for cutting and gathering, threshing and separating the crop. All the driven components are powered by a four-cylinder diesel engine. This 780 model was made at the Kilmarnock Massey-Ferguson factory between 1953 and 1962. It was extremely successful and brought mechanised cereal harvesting to a large number of British farmers. The American companies of Best and Holt built the forerunners to the modern combine harvester in Britain in the 1880s to harvest the wheatlands of California because of a shortage of labour. Combine harvesters were first introduced into the UK in 1928 when three were imported in time for the harvest that year: one built by International Harvester, and two by Massey Harris.

Baird mirror-lid TV

This television, from 1936, looks so large and cumbersome it is difficult to equate it with the sometimes tiny televisions we can buy today. In its time, though, this was the only practical layout for larger screen TVs. Early cathode ray tubes, which were used to make the picture, were longer than the screen diameter, so it made sense to mount the tubes vertically, hence the wooden 'tower'. Since the screen itself was then horizontal, the picture on the screen had to be inverted so that its reflection in the mirror would be seen the right way up.

Bell's Osborne telephone

The inventor Alexander Graham Bell was born in Scotland. He was very interested in the education of deaf people, which led him to invent first the microphone and then, in 1876, his 'electrical speech machine', which we now call a telephone. This beautiful telephone is one of the instruments that Bell used to demonstrate his invention to Queen Victoria at her residence, Osborne House, in 1878. Eager to impress the Queen, Bell made the telephone in walnut and ivory. On early telephones like this one, voices were very faint. It was not until Thomas Edison invented an amplifying carbon microphone that telephones became clearer and long-distance voice communication became a real possibility. The telephone is now such an everyday part of our lives that it is difficult to imagine a time when its presence was a startling and exciting revelation, as it was to Queen Victoria.

Early press camera

By the 1930s, new miniature cameras were on the market. They were light, convenient to carry, and could be used quickly and unobtrusively. They also had large-aperture lenses, making photography under extreme conditions of light possible. A new genre of photojournalism appeared, which exploited the qualities of the miniature cameras to produce pictures more dramatic than had been previously seen, as photographs could be taken spontaneously. In 1938, the *Picture Post* was founded, a magazine featuring 'natural' photos taken by photojournalists. This magazine was extremely influential for 20 years. This Kine Exakta 35 mm, single-lens reflex camera from 1937 was the first of its type. It is the direct ancestor of all modern 35 mm, single-lens cameras.

Vowel Y washing machine and mangle

Thomas Bradford & Co. was the largest manufacturer of washing machinery in the late nineteenth century. Bradford produced a series of washing machines that he called the 'Vowel' series, and had already produced models A, E, I, O and U by 1880. He produced a new machine around 1880 by popular demand. Intending the new machine for people who already had a large heavy mangle, Bradford named his latest model the 'new pattern Vowel Y'. The washing is placed in a hexagonal box sitting on a cast-iron frame, above which is a lightweight, small-roller wringer. The wash box has no agitator inside, only a series of ribs or slats so that, when the box is gently rotated by turning the geared handle, the clothes are tumbled about to remove the dirt. The Vowel Y was a very popular washing machine. It cost £3.15s with the wringer, and £2.10s on its own, making it about half the price of a standard family machine. It could wash eight to ten shirts or a blanket at once, and was even recommended by Mrs Beeton because it did not 'destroy clothes in any way', as the machines with agitators were accused of doing. This actual machine dates back to 1897.

Primitive shell lamp from the Orkneys

Primitive oil lamps were sometimes made from suitably shaped natural materials, such as shells and hollowed-out stones. In remote coastal areas, where resources were scarce, a simple wick could be placed in a shell filled with fish oil. Such shell lamps gave out the same amount of light as a candle. The example shown here was used in the Orkneys as late as the nineteenth century, and contrasts sharply with the elaborate gas and electric lamps that were built in the nineteenth and twentieth centuries.

Viking-style smoothing stone

Before hot irons were invented, people used cold implements to get rid of creases in their clothes. Solid smooth objects, such as animal jaw bones, rounded stones or glass mushrooms were rubbed on washed cloth and linen to 'iron' it. Black glass mushrooms, called 'gnidstein', have been found in eighth-century Viking graves. They were used in England until the early nineteenth century, and were a far cry from the easy-glide steam irons in use today.

Early tin can

The first tin cans for preserving food appeared around 1810, in response to the need of soldiers and explorers to have a means of transporting preserved food in non-breakable containers. The firm of Donkin and Hall set up a 'preservatory' in London, and the new tin-coated wrought-iron cans, by which those away from home could still have a taste of home, were produced. However, the cans were so thick that it was not easy to get the food out – soldiers were reported to have had to attack their cans with knives, bayonets and even rifle fire. Can-openers were not invented until thinner cans appeared in later years. This particular tin can dates from 1823. It was carried on the third Arctic expedition of the explorer William Edward Parry, and was left behind in the Arctic when the crew had to abandon ship. It was found and brought back intact in 1833 by John Ross on returning from his voyage to the Arctic, and apparently used by the Ross family as a doorstop for many years. It was originally thought that this can contained plum pudding but, when it was opened in 1958, it was found to contain roast veal.

History of computer games

In the 1960s, the popularity of arcade game machines initiated the race to produce a viable interactive video game that could be played on a domestic television receiver. As early as 1968 Ralph Baer programmed and patented just such a game, but it wasn't until 1972 that Magnavox marketed a product called 'Odyssey' which sold 100,000 units. Atari (right) was three years old before it entered into a contract with the American retailer Sears. Sears granted it sole distribution rights for the domestic version of 'Pong'. This became the hottest-selling video game of the 1975 Christmas period, grossing around US $40 million. Following the success of these early games, a rush of new companies released many different packages, flooding the domestic market with games such as Space Invaders with its ever-advancing rows of menacing aliens. These companies could satisfy public demand for more difficult and realistic games only by incorporating the newly developed microprocessor. They also took advantage of the technology explosion and the advances in miniaturisation that took place in the 1980s and 1990s. Many of these companies either failed or were taken over by the larger corporations – such as Sony (Playstation),

Sega (Dreamcast) and Nintendo (Nintendo 64). The current products from these companies offer interactive experiences that are very close to the virtual reality experience. The Nintendo 64 can perform 3.5 times as many additions per second as the 1976 Cray-1 supercomputer, and consumes just 5 watts of power as opposed to the Cray's 16,000 watts.

Brownie camera

Eastman–Kodak introduced the Brownie camera in February 1900. This box camera has a simple lens and rotary shutter for time-delayed and instantaneous exposures. It could take six pictures of just over 50mm square from each roll of film. Eastman's previous success was with the pocket Kodak camera. Unfortunately, this camera was too expensive for the average person to afford. Eastman therefore designed the Brownie for mass production, which made them cheaper and available to more people. It sold in England for five shillings (25 p). This simple but efficient camera brought photography within the reach of working people for the first time.

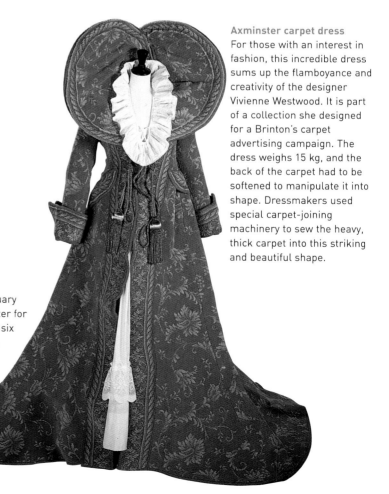

Axminster carpet dress

For those with an interest in fashion, this incredible dress sums up the flamboyance and creativity of the designer Vivienne Westwood. It is part of a collection she designed for a Brinton's carpet advertising campaign. The dress weighs 15 kg, and the back of the carpet had to be softened to manipulate it into shape. Dressmakers used special carpet-joining machinery to sew the heavy, thick carpet into this striking and beautiful shape.

The Aeroscope hand cine camera

This camera, designed by Polish engineer K Proszynski in 1912, was the first completely successful hand cine camera. It could be used in situations where a hand-cranked, tripod-mounted camera was impractical. The Aeroscope is powered by compressed air. Four air cylinders within the body of the camera are charged by means of the portable hand pump. The air from the cylinders drives the camera mechanism. A separate compartment can carry 122 metres of 35 mm film. This camera was used by newsreel cameramen and most of the leading film companies from 1912 until the advent of sound in movies. Visiting cinemas to watch silent movies became a very popular pastime – cameras like this one allowed cameramen to take a greater variety of shots in a wider variety of locations. Cherry Keaton, who marketed the camera in England, used it to take aerial cinematic sequences of London in around 1913.

Radio-gramophone

In the 1880s, Emile Berliner demonstrated a machine which played flat discs. The ripples of the grooves were side to side instead of up and down as in phonograph cylinders. The gramophone eventually superseded the phonograph because the flat discs were easier to produce in quantity and were more easily handled and stored. Discs which turned at 78 revolutions per minute were the standard playing disc, until vinyl long-playing records were introduced in 1948. In the 1930s, the National Grid made it possible for an increasing number of households to receive AC mains electricity. This kind of electricity was ideal for making machines, such as gramophones, run at fixed speeds. An AC motor drove the foldaway turntable of this 1932 'Micro-perephone radio-gramophone'. The inside edge of the turntable has magnetic 'teeth', driven directly by coils carrying mains current, so there are no belts and pulleys which could cause distortion, known as 'wow' or 'flutter'.

Audio tutu

Benoit Maubrey invented this audio tutu in 1989 as part of his concept in electro-acoustic or audio clothes. Dancers wear such tutus to record the sound patterns of their movements. The electronics in the tutu digitally alter the sound, turning it into music for the dance. The tutu, which is solar-powered and made of Plexi-glas, contains a microphone and speakers. Maubrey and his colleagues, working at Audio Gruppe in Germany, have developed many ideas and designs into tools for public performance. For example, they created audio bicycles for cyclists, who performed at the Arts Festival in Rennes.

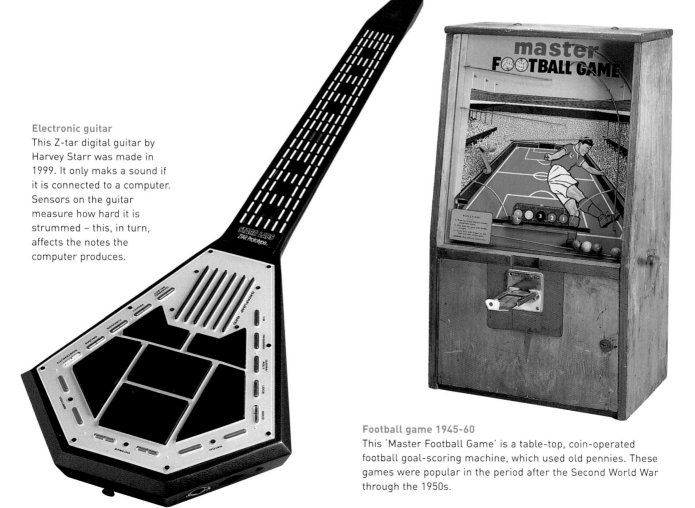

Electronic guitar

This Z-tar digital guitar by Harvey Starr was made in 1999. It only maks a sound if it is connected to a computer. Sensors on the guitar measure how hard it is strummed – this, in turn, affects the notes the computer produces.

Football game 1945-60

This 'Master Football Game' is a table-top, coin-operated football goal-scoring machine, which used old pennies. These games were popular in the period after the Second World War through the 1950s.

Robot pit

These robots, created at the Department of Cybernetics, University of Reading, appear to be able to think as they move around seemingly independently. In fact, they use ultrasonic sensors, much like those used by bats, to detect objects and make sure they don't crash into things. They also have the ability to 'talk' to each other using infrared signals, which the human ear cannot detect. Within the group, the robots indicate their location, so they are aware of each other's presence. They are intended as a kind of toy, as users can control their behaviour by means of a joystick. For example, users can make the robots chase after them, or each other, and lead them in a synchronised dance. These robots can be found in the 'robot pit' in the Museum, where they provide a unique form of entertainment.

'Talk With Me!' Barbie doll, 1997

Mattel launched this version of the ever-popular Barbie doll for Christmas 1997. Barbie's own computer links to the serial port of the user's computer. By inserting the CD-ROM, the user gives Barbie the power of speech, and can select a range of topics for Barbie to memorise. This information is then downloaded into Barbie by an ultraviolet beam, which travels from the computer screen to her necklace. Barbie had her fortieth birthday in 1999 and remains one of the most popular dolls, as she constantly evolves to reflect the times.

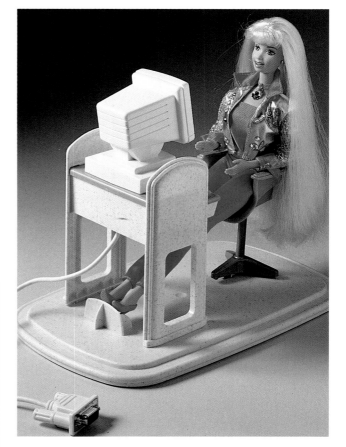

Dinky toys

In the 1960s the toy industry prospered through its ability to mass-produce metal and plastic toys. Most of the demand resulted from the impact of TV and cinema in generating mass markets for licensed products. Meccano made Dinky toys, such as this 'Thunderbird 2' and Lady Penelope's pink car 'Fab 1', inspired by Gerry Anderson's *Thunderbirds* series.

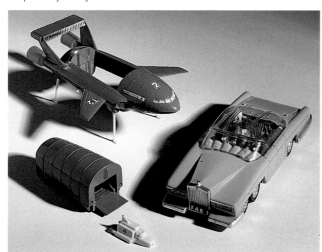

Museum

There is more to a museum than meets the eye. This section gives a behind-the-scenes glimpse at activities that contribute to the day-to-day running of the Science Museum. Such activities include the work of the conservation staff in taking care of the Museum's collections, and the role of the Education department. We discuss the processes involved in the development of a new gallery and the vision behind the newest addition to the Museum – the Wellcome Wing. An example of an historical experiment undertaken at the Museum is the latest stage in the project to build the calculating machines invented and designed, but never completed by, Charles Babbage. We give a short history of the Museum, and briefly describe the other branches of the National Museum of Science & Industry. In addition, one selection shows artefacts that are slightly unusual and not what a visitor might expect to see in a science museum. Finally, we show a small number of the works in the Museum's amazing art collection, which documents the historical events that have shaped technological and scientific change.

Queen Victoria opening the Great Exhibition in 1851. This plate is taken from the *Illustrated London News* (Vol. 51).

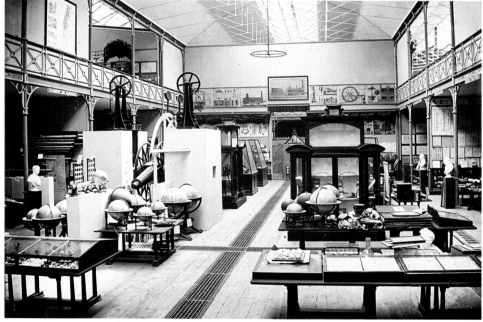

Astronomical equipment at the South Kensington Museum, *c.* 1860.

History of the Science Museum

The year 2001 marks the 150th anniversary of the Great Exhibition. The Exhibition was set up to display the products of the Industrial Revolution from every developed nation, and was the first step in the history of the Science Museum. The Exhibition's success led to demands for an institution to educate the public in arts and sciences, and keep them informed on the vital role played by science and industry in the prosperity of their nation. The Treasury set up the Department of Science and Art in 1853 which, in 1857, was transferred to the care of the Committee of the Privy Council of Education.

Collections were bought from the Great Exhibition and the Government School of Design. These were transferred to South Kensington in 1856, into a corrugated iron building, together with art collections from the Museum of Ornamental Art at Marlborough House. Queen Victoria opened these premises in 1857 as the South Kensington Museum. The collections were not representative of the whole field of physical and applied science but consisted of an educational selection of books and models, a collection of animal products, a food exhibition, a collection of astronomical equipment and, from 1864, a small collection of naval models and marine engines.

The Patent Office Museum, in the remaining 'Old Brompton Boilers' buildings, South Kensington, *c.* 1876.

This first South Kensington Museum stood on the site now occupied by the Victoria and Albert Museum. The original buildings became known as the 'Brompton Boilers' because they resembled steam boilers. The collections were cramped and visitors found it difficult to view them properly. As a result, in 1872 the Brompton Boilers were re-erected, with improved walls made of brick instead of corrugated iron, at a new site in Bethnal Green. This building housed the Animal Products collection, the Food collection and several art collections, pieces of which later became publicly known as the Wallace Collection. The remaining part of the Brompton Boilers in South Kensington housed the Patent Office Museum, which acquired some of the most famous engineering exhibits, such as *Puffing Billy* and *Rocket*.

The South Kensington site continued to develop as various exhibitions between 1862 and 1874 led to the building of several galleries, parts of which still make up a section of the buildings in the current Victoria and Albert Museum. The science collections in the South Kensington Museum continued to grow, though in rather a haphazard fashion.

In 1875, the Committee of Council of Education approved a proposal to create a consolidated collection of scientific apparatus, to include equipment for teaching and also objects of historic interest. A science exhibition was held a year later, which displayed scientific instruments of all kinds from many countries and hosted lectures on the progress of various sciences. Over the next few years, the scientific and machinery collections were merged, and the educational apparatus used for class instruction was dispersed.

A Select Committee, established in 1897, recommended that the science and art collections be separated, with the art collections to the east of Exhibition Road and the science collections to the west. Queen Victoria laid the foundation stone for the new building of industrial art on the east side, which became known as the Victoria and Albert Museum at her request.

The entrance to the Science Museum, at the far right of this picture, on the west side of Exhibition Road, *c.*1905.

The Science Museum viewed from Exhibition Road.

A committee chaired by Sir Hugh Bell recommended that the science collections should be greatly expanded, including the addition of an oceanography gallery. The Bell Committee also suggested the inclusion of as many models as possible, demonstration rooms, and space for special temporary exhibitions. The building itself should contain spacious halls and several galleries for detailed presentation of the various branches of science and technology. These recommendations began to take shape by 1913, but the First World War put a stop to the building's use as a museum. Instead, the structural shell of the building was used for government office space, and the galleries continued to be used as offices for some time after the war. Technology, particularly in aeronautics, had raced ahead during the war and the Museum now had to face the prospect of housing whole new collections. Pure science had also leapt ahead, with the splitting of the atom and the development of new drugs. The new block of the Science Museum was finally opened in March 1928.

During the Second World War practically all of the Museum objects were evacuated to country homes to avoid damage in the London air raids. The building was used as a Royal Air Force signals school. By 1951, in time for the Festival of Britain, the ground floor of the centre block had been built to house the science section of the Festival exhibition before it was handed over to the Science Museum. The remaining floors of the centre block were added between 1959 and 1961.

Puffing Billy and *Caerphilly Castle* locomotives in the *Land Transport* gallery, which closed in 1996.

Since 1951, there have been many changes to the galleries inside the Museum. For example, various galleries have been altered, removed or added, including the Wellcome galleries depicting the history of medicine (opened in 1980 and 1981), the *Exploration of Space* gallery (opened in 1986) and *Challenge of Materials* (opened in 1997).

In the early days of the Science Museum, Warders looked like policemen. These days their uniforms are less formal.

Science and technology are constantly developing and changing. The Science Museum collections reflect this through frequent updates and the addition of new galleries. In July 2000, the Wellcome Wing at the Science Museum opened to become a leading centre for the presentation of modern science and technology. The Wing encompasses 10,000 m² of space, increasing the total floor area of the Museum by a third. The old Land Transport gallery closed in 1996 to make way for a new gallery, *Making the Modern World*, which opened along with the Wellcome Wing. This gallery portrays 250 years of the cultural history of industrialisation, and includes some of the objects displayed in the Great Exhibition of 1851.

The Wellcome Wing under construction, November 1998.

The Wellcome Wing

The opening of the Wellcome Wing on 3 July 2000 signified the successful completion of the Science Museum's largest and most ambitious project to date. After ten years of planning, research and consultation, the Wing opened to become a leading centre for the public presentation of contemporary science.

The vision

The vision behind the development of the new wing was to create a 'breathtaking theatre of contemporary science'. This would continue the original dream of the founders of the Science Museum – to create an institution that addresses the importance of science, technology, industry and medicine – into the new millennium, reinterpreting the dream to apply to a new age and new technologies.

The vast, blue glass wall reduces light levels.

The *Antenna* gallery responds to new developments in science as they happen.

The design

With this vision in mind, the architects created a unique environment in which to house the three exhibition floors and IMAX cinema. Inside a 10,000 m² space (larger than two football pitches), the choice of materials and use of light has created a dramatic setting in which the exhibition floors appear to float in space.

The subtle lighting in the wing is provided in an ingenious way. At the west end of the building is a vast, blue glass wall that can reduce light levels, even in the summer, to those required for exhibitions. The side walls are also suffused with deep blue lights, caught and diffused by a special glass-fibre material. The careful balance between natural and artificial light provides ideal conditions for individual exhibits to be displayed to best effect.

Steel beams and gerberettes (cantilevers) provide the framework on which the exhibition floors are visibly suspended. The combination of the blue light and the translucent materials used in the interior construction heightens the effect of transparency and weightlessness. Even the under-surfaces of the exhibition floors and IMAX cinema are transparent, consisting of a fine steel grille in an opaque material. The IMAX cinema has a huge underbelly, which appears to soar over visitors' heads. The escalator up to the cinema is positioned to provide visitors with a panoramic view of the whole area.

Interactives

The Wellcome Wing presents exhibits and communicates ideas to the public in a new way. In a frequently-updated, interactive environment, visitors can become involved in the content of the exhibits in a variety of ways.

The *Antenna* gallery is updated on a monthly, weekly, daily and even instantaneous basis, giving visitors access to new developments in science as they happen. The fastest response comes from a series of rapidly evolving exhibits that track important science stories as these unfold. Meanwhile, thematic exhibits explore major topics in depth. There is also a continually updated bulletin board, supported by leading science news services. Informal demonstrations and regular events, in which the scientists and technologists themselves discuss their work, complete this exciting and informative gallery.

Visitors can also take part in real scientific research in the Live Science area of the biomedical gallery *Who am I?*. They can contribute to this research by volunteering as participants. The first of these projects to be carried out was conducted by David Hopkinson of the Galton Laboratory at University College, London. By scanning the faces of visitors and taking DNA samples using cheek swabs, he aimed to identify the genes that control people's facial features and give rise to similarities between family members.

Visitors are able to create their own website and store information that they have built up by using the interactive exhibits. They can also give their views on scientific issues at feedback points throughout the Wing. Under-8s can play and learn in a hands-on gallery called *Pattern Pod* which encourages children to develop skills such as recognising, copying, manipulating and creating patterns.

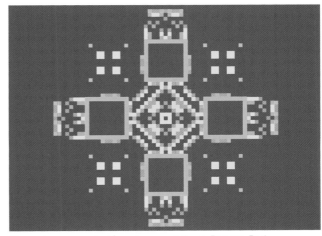

Computer-generated 'magic carpet' from *Pattern Pod*.

In Future consists of three circular, interactive tables at which groups of visitors can consider dilemmas raised by new science and technology, thereby creating imaginary futures out of the decisions they make.

The *Digitopolis* gallery provides a stimulating introduction to the digital technology that has come to define our age.

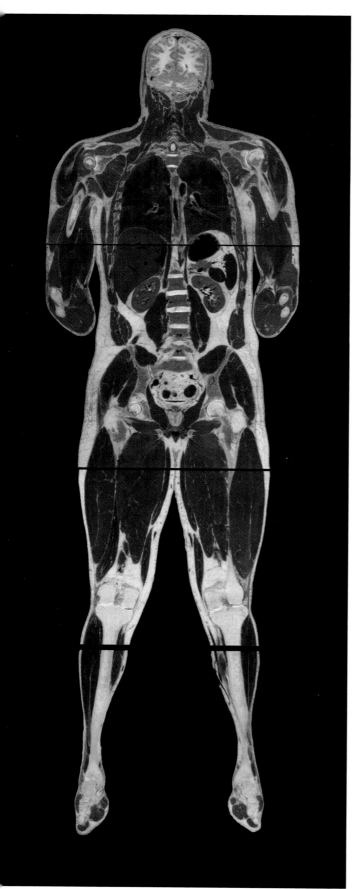

Image from the Visible Human project.

Artefacts

The Wellcome Wing incorporates objects that have played a major role in modern science. Some important artefacts on display for the first time include the computer on which the World Wide Web was designed and the equipment used in the Human Genome Project to map DNA.

In *Who am I?*, the remains of an Iron Age man, discovered in Bleadon, Somerset, help to explain what DNA studies might reveal about visitors' genetic relationships to this 2000-year-old relic (see page 41). In Sounds Digital, part of the *Digitopolis* gallery, a digital tutu is one of several musical instruments that illustrate developments in digital technology (see page 62). *Talking Points* introduces another pioneering presentation technique. In a series of one-off exhibits, objects intended to provoke debate and discussion are displayed, for example Mika Hakkinen's Formula 1 car, which crashed in the 1999 German Grand Prix. The Visible Human project allows visitors to view digital cross-sections of the human body.

Mika Hakkinen's Formula 1 car, *Talking Points*.

Euthanasia machine, *Talking Points*.

Art

Contemporary art is an important feature of the Wellcome Wing. On display, as part of the exhibitions, are new commissions and purchased works from internationally renowned artists. The sculptures, works on paper, photographs and installations are integrated with scientific storylines. They have been included to challenge and surprise visitors, to encourage debate and to enrich the environment.

The ground floor includes new works by Darrell Viner (*Is Tall Better than Small?*), Yinka Shonibare (*Effective, Defective, Creative*), Marc Quinn (*Eternal Spring II: Sunflowers*) and Scanner (*Sound Curtain*). These form part of the *Talking Points* family of exhibits.

A series of small-scale art works can be found throughout the *Who am I?* gallery. They include purchases from Antony Gormley (*Iron Baby*), Marlene Dumas (*The Experiment* and *The Expert*) and Angus Fairhurst (*Things That Don't Work Properly* and *Things That Never Stop*). There are also new commissions from

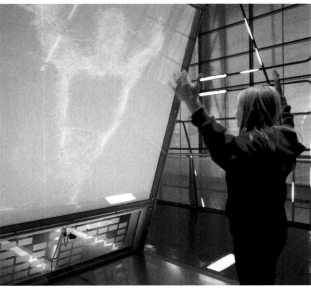

Particles by Christian Möller.

Iron Baby by Antony Gormley.

David Shrigley (objects, drawings and photographs including *I Have Swallowed a Piece of Lego*) and Wendy McMurdo (*XX – Who am I? gallery, Science Museum, London 2000*).

A large-scale video installation by Gary Hill can be found in the north stairwell. This work was also specially commissioned. It consists of a repeated motif of individuals gazing at their hands, projected on to an 18-metre-high wall.

Composer Nye Parry was commissioned to perform a new work in the *Who am I?* gallery. This electro-acoustic composition can be heard in the Wellcome Wing's south staircase. Parry's piece shares the staircase with artist Peter Sedgley's *Interplanes*, a kinetic sculpture that casts coloured light onto the surrounding walls.

The Science Museum is now one of the major non-art institutions worldwide to include contemporary art on this scale. The Museum intends to build on this by developing projects with artists in future displays.

HanD HearD – Variation by Gary Hill.

The completed gallery, July 2000.

The *Making the Modern World* gallery under construction, February 2000.

The creation of *Making the Modern World*

The preparation of a permanent Science Museum gallery normally takes several years. From the initial idea – through the appointment of a curatorial team, designers and builders – to its opening, many specialists become involved in detailed study, discussion, selection and composition. *Making the Modern World* is the largest single gallery the Museum has produced in many years. In scope, it is also the broadest, drawing on the Museum's unparalleled collections from heavy engineering to fine art, and from bio-engineered mice to atom-smashers.

This gallery is really four exhibitions in one, all following the same chronology from the early years of industrialisation in 1750 to the eve of the twenty-first century. The main boulevard of this huge, cathedral-like space is filled with some 150 iconic objects from the Museum's collections. Acting as a counterpoint to these special and significant objects, a parallel display, showing the technology we encounter in everyday life, is positioned to the north. To the south are nine subsidiary displays, which explore in greater depth some of the stories behind the icons. The gallery is completed by a display of 'technology in miniature' on a raised walkway running the full length of the gallery, carrying 150 models.

The Age of the Engineer display case in
Making the Modern World.

The mock-up for the display of technology in everyday life,
1880–1939, in the Science Museum's West London store.

Overall, the gallery contains in the region of 2000 objects
– the selection of such objects is one of the curators'
main tasks. Each display strand in this gallery required
its own selection process but, in each case, the lists of
objects drawn up were the result of practical as well as
intellectual factors. For example, an object that was
considered important may have been too heavy, too
difficult to make safe or visually too unprepossessing to
include. In the 'theme' displays to the south, relatively
small and sometimes provocative artefacts were often
chosen to symbolise an area of technology too large, or a
subject too abstract, for any other form of representation.

In the preparations for this exhibition, Museum staff
created 'mock-up' displays off-site, a technique that
became a crucial part of the development process. At the
Museum's west London storage building, curators built
full-size replicas of the areas in the gallery that now
contain the five 'everyday technology' and nine 'theme'
displays. Working closely with the architects and the
graphics consultants, curators produced object
selections, stories, display furniture and labelling
schemes for all 14 sub-exhibits. This allowed them to try
out their ideas and make modifications until the desired
result was achieved.

View of the model walkway.

Conservation at the Science Museum

One of the primary functions of the Museum is to preserve the artefacts in its collections as physical records of the history and development of science, industry and medicine. The staff of the conservation section work behind the scenes to clean, conserve and repair these objects, and regularly check those on display for signs of damage or deterioration. If any deterioration is found, the artefacts are removed to the laboratory where the skilled conservators treat them in order to preserve the original material, structure and historic evidence. Conservators also work on objects required for future exhibitions at the Science Museum and at other institutions, and those needed for research by scholars and students.

The Museum is responsible for two other sites, at Wroughton in Wiltshire and the West London store, where further objects are stored. These sites both have conservation facilities where the staff monitor the condition of the collections and conserve any objects that are deteriorating.

Once an object has been conserved or put into storage it must not continue to deteriorate. Heat, relative humidity, visible and ultraviolet light, atmospheric pollutants and insects all affect the materials the objects are made from. The collections-care team, working with other Museum staff, ensure that the collections are kept in stable, clean conditions.

Many motor vehicles are kept at the Science Museum site at Wroughton. Here, a member of the Wroughton conservation staff prepares an Indian motorcycle for storage.

Science Museum conservation staff cleaned, repaired and reassembled this model of a nineteenth-century workshop. In this picture, a conservator discusses the cleaning of the many small model parts with the Museum archivist. The model was conserved for exhibition in the *Making the Modern World* gallery.

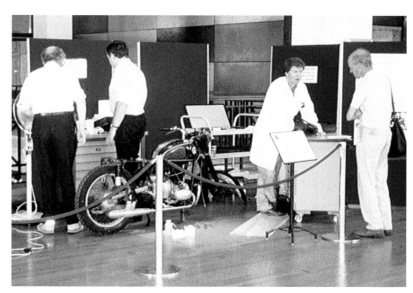

Conservation department open days, for which a workshop was set up in one of the Museum galleries. Visitors were able to see the processes involved, and ask the conservators questions about their work.

The historic Panhard and Levassor motor car was cleaned and conserved for display in the *Making the Modern World* gallery. A conservator carefully reassembles the engine after painstakingly cleaning the intricate engine parts.

Large objects suspended from the ceiling in the *Flight* gallery are cleaned on site.

Many people might think that conservation has more to do with archaeology or works of art, such as paintings, than with industrial or scientific objects. However, the modern materials used to make some of the objects collected by the Museum are as difficult to conserve as some of the things found in archaeological digs. The Science Museum works with people from industry, universities and other museums to try and find methods of preserving modern materials such as plastics.

The conservators also bring their work out into the open in the Museum galleries for visitors to see during Museum open days. They are happy to answer questions about their work, so that visitors can see how the collections are preserved and have the chance to witness what goes on behind the scenes at the Museum.

When the old *Land Transport* gallery in the Science Museum was cleared away to make room for new exhibits, many of the objects had to be packed very carefully so they could be transported to storage facilities without being damaged.

Charles Babbage's Difference Engine No. 2, constructed at the Science Museum from original designs dating from 1847–49. The printing and stereotyping apparatus, completed in 2001, is shown in the foreground. The calculating section, completed in 1991 for the bicentennial year of Babbage's birth, can be seen at the rear.

Experimenting with history

Charles Babbage (1791–1871), the English mathematician, is widely celebrated as the 'father of computing'. The designs for his vast mechanical calculating engines rank as one of the startling achievements of his age. But, despite his genius, generous government funding and decades of design and development, Babbage failed to construct a complete machine. A question remained unanswered for over 140 years: if he had completed a calculating engine, would it have worked? In 1991, the bicentennial year of Babbage's birth, the first Babbage Engine was built to original designs and completed at the Science Museum. The project took six years to complete. The engine is Difference Engine No. 2 designed by Babbage between 1847 and 1849.

The calculating section of the Engine consists of 4000 parts, weighs 2.6 tonnes and measures 3.5 metres long and 2 metres high. It works without fault.

The full design also includes a massive printing apparatus, completed in 2001. This apparatus automatically prints a copy of results on paper, and produces printing moulds for use in a conventional printing press.

The printer consists of a further 4000 parts and the full machine is estimated to weigh 5 tonnes. It is completely mechanical and is remarkable in that it allows the user to alter the layout of results on the page automatically. The device can print in one, two or three columns, print across the page and automatically line wrap to the start of the next line, or print down the page and automatically fly back to the top of the next column. The user can alter the space between lines and the width of the margins. It also prints in two sizes of type simultaneously. Engineers worked on the machine in public view and ran trials throughout 2000.

With the completion of the printer, visitors are able to behold what no Victorian ever saw – a complete Babbage engine in all its splendour: a fitting tribute to a remarkable pioneer.

Science Museum engineers working on Babbage's Difference Engine No. 2.

Assembling the printing apparatus for Charles Babbage's Difference Engine No. 2, February 2000. Engineers guide a section of the printing mechanism into place using a gantry.

The printing mechanism for Babbage's Difference Engine No. 2, completed in March 2001.

Montgolfier balloon

This stunning model of a balloon was built around 1900 and is
a small-scale replica of the original balloon, built by the
Montgolfier brothers in 1783. The balloon was the first to be
used in a public demonstration of flight when the brothers, in
the presence of King Louis XIV and Marie Antoinette, flew it
carrying a sheep, a duck and a cockerel. The balloon was
made of paper and cloth and beautifully decorated. Today,
ballooning is considered one of the most peaceful and
romantic ways to fly, and this model seems to encapsulate the
romance of one of the earliest forms of flight.

Butlins souvenir tankard

This small glass tankard was made for the Butlins Christmas
1961 period. At the end of the Second World War, Billy Butlin
bought back from the government the camps he had built for the
army to use. He opened them as holiday camps, offering a week
of fresh air and regimented fun.

Collycroft worsted mill model

Until the late eighteenth century, manufacturers requiring power
built works close to water. This model illustrates the way in which
the water wheel was integrated into many early factories, the
power being distributed from the wheel throughout the building.
Even when the steam engine became a satisfactory alternative,
industries often continued to be concentrated in the traditional
areas where, for various reasons, available water power might
remain preferable to steam power. This is why the British textile
industry relied more on water power than on the steam engine,
even as late as the second half of the nineteenth century.

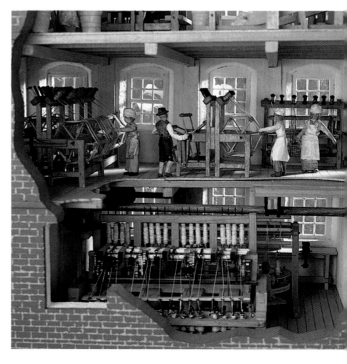

Materials House

This amazing sculpture is 'the world's largest composite sandwich of materials'. It was built specifically for the Museum and contains a great variety of materials. In total, there are 213 layers, all of which vary in colour and texture. Each layer has been cut so that it reveals the surface of its constituent part only once. The towering sculpture leans at a 65-degree angle. The overall effect, from the foot of the materials house, is of a fascinating mass of curving, colourful waves. The model is so complex that it took four months to program a computer to produce the design. The latest water-cutting technology was used to create the high-tolerance profiles. Layers of wood were planed down to 6 mm and laminated together, before being cut out using MDF templates as a guide. The designers chose materials that were non-toxic, would not decompose, and would not disintegrate when they were worked. One layer consists of leaves, collected from a local park, which were bonded to the wood template and sealed with three coats of varnish. Each layer was mechanically fixed using 500 bolts, 6000 screws and hundreds of litres of contact adhesive. The end result is an impressive and eye-catching sculpture.

Water jar, or hydria

This south Italian (Apulian) water jar dates from the mid-fifth to the fourth century BC. It is beautifully preserved, and decorated with the figures of two women beside an altar adorned with funeral offerings. The cups belong to the same set, and are some of the oldest objects held in the Museum collections.

Glass objects

This beautiful collection of glass objects shows the variety of textures, shapes and shades it is possible to create with glass. From the Venetian bottle (bottom centre), which dates from 1600, to the ruby-cased glass dome (right), which was specially commissioned for the Science Museum in 1988, the collection represents a fascinating and eye-catching history of the use of glass. Also shown are a Roman flask from AD 150–300 (below left), a mouth-blown, hand-made doorstop from 1964 (below right), and a Spanish flask (far right) inscribed with the date 1492.

Burmese elephant weights

These decorative weights, in the shape of elephants, date from the seventeenth century.

'Ballooniana'

The success of the first amazing balloon trips in Paris, 1783, gave professional showmen a new means of earning a living – holding public balloon ascents. These spectacles were often held in pleasure gardens and attracted huge crowds. They had a powerful impact on those who watched and led, in turn, to 'ballooniana', or balloon art, expressed in paintings, prints and decorated ceramics as well as many other forms. The selection shown here is from the fine Penn-Gaskell collection of ceramics, medals and decorative objects commemorating balloon flight. The objects date from 1783 to 1983.

Opera glasses

This selection of prospect glasses dates from the third quarter of the eighteenth century. The materials used to make these glasses include shagreen, vellum, lacquered ivory, leather, horn, silver, fish skin, burr walnut and brass. Prospect glasses are small Galilean telescopes, which became popular as a status symbol in the eighteenth century. They increasingly became known as opera glasses. They remained unaffected by the optical advances taking place in scientific instruments, and changed only in style – for example, brass was used instead of vellum in the draw tubes of later models.

The Pictorial Collection

Pictures have been collected in the Science Museum from its early days. They are as valued as any other object in the Museum, thanks to the historical or technical importance of their subject content, or as a documentary record of artefacts, events and developments within science and industry.

After a century or so of collecting up to 200,000 works, the Science Museum established the Pictorial Collection in 1977. Its brief is to acquire, conserve, store, research, catalogue, interpret and display the collection, to enable general visitors and researchers to access the works. Pictures held in store are viewable by appointment.

An oil portrait of James Watt (1736–1819) by Carl von Breda, 1792.

A bronze bust of Albert Einstein (1879–1955) by Jacob Epstein.

The Comet of 1532, an inscribed watercolour.

Although not directly concerned with aesthetics, much of the collection has great visual appeal and is worthy of exhibiting in its own right. The emphasis for collecting new pieces today is still primarily on content rather than aesthetics or medium. However, many pictures, and some artists, are also now recognised as important in the genre of British art, and a growing number of works are internationally known.

Some works are by artists who have been inspired in their creativity by science and industry. The oil painting *Coalbrookdale by Night* by Loutherbourg (see p.8) is a key example.

At the heart of the collection are prints, drawings, paintings, portraits, printed ephemera, cartographic items and some sculpture – items which range from stamps to murals. Much material is unique or rare. Some pieces are very old, acting like windows on the past, while others look to the future. Until recent years the focus of collecting was historical, especially upon the Industrial Revolution period, and predominantly national. Currently the collection has a global outlook and is developing its twentieth- and twenty-first-century holdings.

An early nineteenth-century watercolour depicting miners at the face of a lead mine in Alston Moor, Northumberland.

Cycles Automoto St Etienne
– a poster, *c.* 1914, by Tamagno.

The Picture Gallery

Why is there an art gallery in a science museum? The Picture Gallery is not merely an 'art' gallery, but a little oasis of space dedicated to showing some of the Science Museum's pictorial, and related, collections to visitors. Works can be viewed out of the stores, with conditions of display and calm which are not easy to find in the major galleries of the Museum. The gallery opened in 1992.

Picture galleries came into use in private homes from about the seventeenth century. They were spaces with walls suitable for hanging paintings, such as family portraits and landscapes, often in dense rows right up to the ceiling. As collections grew, spaces grew larger and were purpose-built. The picture gallery became a natural accessory for eighteenth-century gentlemen, alongside a 'cabinet of curiosities' or mini-museum of sciences, an observatory and the study library with finely-bound books, maps and folios of engravings.

The Gallery has presented more than 20 exhibitions to date, in many media, ranging from historical subjects to contemporary installations and artists in residence, within a rolling programme. Comments on exhibitions and ideas for future displays are welcomed from visitors.

The National Railway Museum, York.

The NRM, York

The National Railway Museum is the largest railway museum in the world, and holds many railway icons together with millions of artefacts. This huge collection, including 103 locomotives and 177 other items of rolling stock, traces the evolution of the railway from the first steam locomotives to Eurostar. The collections include a variety of Royal saloons dating back to the pre-Victorian era, many famous locomotives and carriages, a 'permanent way' timeline, historic signalling equipment, and even a section of the Channel Tunnel. The national collections include a host of other artefacts associated with our railways, such as 3300 models, 6500 items of silver and crockery, over 300 nameplates, 350,000 tickets, 1800 buttons, 1.4 million negatives, 350,000 engineering drawings, 7500 posters and 200 original works of art. It also hosts a vast archive of documents.

The National Museum of Photography, Film & Television, Bradford

The NMPFT is an interactive museum aimed at everyone who has ever taken a photograph or been photographed, who has been to the cinema or watched television. A mixture of hands-on displays and galleries about the art and science of photography are clustered around a giant IMAX cinema screen. The exhibits encourage visitors not only to look at objects and learn about the history and techniques of photography, but also to think about the processes involved in creating the visual images that surround us. In 1998, the NMPFT was redeveloped, with a £16 million backing from the Heritage Lottery Fund, the Arts Council of England, the Foundation for Sport and the Arts, the European Union and private investment. The Museum is now in step with the increasing influence of digital technology on photography, film and television. Visitors can explore and interact with digital technology, learning how computers and telecommunications play a vital role in imagery.

The NMPFT, Bradford.

West London store

The Science Museum houses its smaller collections in its West London store. Here, about 100 storerooms occupy 9000 square metres of floor space, on six levels. Objects are stored on open racks or glazed cupboards, so that staff and visitors can easily see them. Some larger objects are free-standing. The collections are more accessible than if they were kept in boxes or crates, and conservators can easily monitor their condition. To keep out light, dirt, insects and moisture, windows in the store are covered and sealed. Even the paint on the shelving and the foam used to support fragile items are carefully chosen to ensure they will not go yellow, crumble or give off vapours that could damage the objects. Objects from all areas of the Museum's collections are stored here, including some particularly fine examples from the astronomy, aeronautics and medical collections. Visitors are welcome by appointment, and tours can be arranged for groups.

Part of the Farnborough collection in the Science Museum's West London store.

Wroughton

At Wroughton Airfield, near Swindon in Wiltshire, the Science Museum houses its collections of large objects in store and on display. These include commercial aircraft, vintage cars and motorbikes, space rockets, Wurlitzers, traction engines and valve computers. Located on a Second World War airfield, several hangars contain a collection of fascinating objects which represent key developments in science and technology. Throughout the year a number of outdoor events take place at the airfield, during which time the collection may be accessible to the public. Wroughton airfield was originally opened in 1940 as a base to modify and prepare aircraft for front-line stations in the Second World War. It became the Royal Naval Aircraft Yard, Wroughton, in 1972 when the navy became responsible for servicing helicopters from all three services, and finally closed in 1978. In the mid 1970s the Science Museum, investigating ways of finding more space for storage and display of objects, decided to purchase the Wroughton site. It was large enough to allow the Museum to acquire civil aircraft and develop its other collections, including road transport and agricultural engineering.

The Science Museum formally took over the airfield and six hangars on 1 May 1980.

Entrance to the Imperial College & Science Museum Libraries.

The Science Museum Library

The Science Museum Library was founded in 1883 and, in 1992, linked its building with the adjacent Central Libraries of Imperial College of Science, Technology and Medicine to form the Imperial College & Science Museum Libraries. Science Museum Library staff work closely with Imperial College to provide a coordinated system of shared stock and services. Nowadays the focus of the Science Museum Library is the Science and Technology Studies collection. Although it is a research library, it is open to the public for reference, and operates a worldwide mail-order information and photocopy service in the history and public understanding of science and technology. The Science Museum's archive collection is also based in the library. It complements the object collections and maintains an archive of the Museum's own history.

An AEC Major eight-wheel tanker from 1934 being prepared for an open day at Wroughton.

Education

The Royal Commission, which was established after the Great Exhibition of 1851, proposed that a permanent institution should be created to 'increase the means of industrial education and extend the influence of Science and Art upon productive industry'. The aim of this institution, which eventually became the Science Museum, was, from the start, to provide an important source of technical education. Over time that aim has been extended by increasing the emphasis on the historical aspects of technology, and by designing exhibitions and providing educational services for a general, rather than a technical, audience. With the opening of the Wellcome Wing in particular, the Museum's educational role increasingly emphasises contemporary science and technology together with historical perspectives.

Actors demonstrate balloon flight in one of the Museum's drama shows in the *Flight* gallery.

An Explainer uses a 'water rocket' to demonstrate Newton's Third Law of Motion to children in *Flight Lab*.

Families

Families are a core audience for the Science Museum. Exhibitions are designed to offer something to interest and engage all family members. 'Explainers' are on hand in the more interactive exhibitions to encourage interaction and explain the exhibits. During school holidays and at weekends, informal events and regular Science Shows and drama activities offer additional opportunities to complement the exhibitions. Perhaps best known of all are the Science Nights – sleepovers for 8–11-year-olds and their parents or carers, which are run on a monthly basis.

Students mix their own radio show and learn about radio communication in the *On Air* gallery.

Students gather information on materials that protect the body in the *Challenge of Materials* gallery.

Students

In one sense each visitor is a student, since everyone visits a place like a museum with a desire to learn. Special events and activity sheets are available for school groups, and Explainers are always on hand in the interactive galleries to respond to questions. For adult learners, the wider resources of the Museum are also available, such as the Science Museum Library and seminars in the history of science and technology.

Outreach

Activities and exhibitions are regularly toured throughout the UK. They are taken into places as diverse as schools for children with special educational needs, or shopping malls. The Science Museum also led the way in adapting its exhibitions for a European audience. Its first such exhibition was *Future Foods?*, which was tailored to each venue by collaborating with the venue itself and leading experts in the biomedical field. In this way, the Museum reaches new audiences.

A group of school students gather with their teacher inside the schools' entrance of the Science Museum.

Teachers

The Science Museum welcomes around 300,000 visitors in pre-booked educational groups each year, more than any other museum in the UK. Teachers from pre-school to further- and higher-education levels accompany groups of students, helping to bring the curriculum to life. The Museum provides support for these teachers in the form of information, teaching resources and courses. The Museum also makes every effort to accommodate individual interests and needs.

Internet

The Science Museum has pioneered the use of the Internet for educational purposes, from online booking by teachers to online resources, activities and conferences. Flagship activities include the STEM (Students' and Teachers' Educational Materials) project (http://www.sciencemuseum.org.uk/education/stem). This encourages teachers and students to publish on the Web their perspectives on the educational use of the Museum. In addition, the Science Learning Network (http://www.sciencemuseum.org.uk/education/sln) is an international partnership of science museums to produce science learning experiences on the Web.

Index

List of objects

The following objects from the Science Museum's collections are shown in this book. The figures in brackets are Museum inventory numbers.

Sponsors, Donors and Corporate Partners

The Science Museum would like to thank the following organisations for their generous support:

Sponsors and Donors

The Heritage Lottery Fund
The Wellcome Trust
The UK Steel Industry
The Garfield Weston Foundation
Intel

Agfa UK
BBC
The Engineering and
Physical Sciences Research Council
GlaxoSmithKline
Pfizer
Toshiba

The Aluminium Federation
ICI

The British Psychological Society
ExxonMobil Gas Marketing
Dollond & Aitchison
Nature

The Clothworkers' Foundation
The Zochonis Charitable Trust

Corporate Partners

Patron
British Telecommunications plc
GlaxoSmithKline
TAG McLaren Holdings Ltd
The UK Steel Industry

Benefactor
Consignia
ExxonMobil Gas Marketing
John Lewis Partnership
Kyocera

Member
Akzo Nobel
American Express
Barclays
Cable & Wireless plc
Drivers Jonas
N M Rothschild & Sons Ltd
Smiths Group plc

Associate
Agenda Design Associates
CMS Cameron McKenna
DS Print & Redesign
Farrer & Co
Ove Arup Partnership
Tranter Lowe
Walfords